# Locomotive Traction

2018

Pip Dunn

Crécy.co.uk

First published by Crécy Publishing Limited
2017



A CIP record for this book is available from the British Library

**ISBN 9781910809501**

Printed in England by LatimerTrend

**abc is an imprint of**
**Crécy Publishing Limited**
1a Ringway Trading Estate
Shadowmoss Road
Manchester M22 5LH

**www.crecy.co.uk**

*Front Cover Top:* DRS 68009 *Titan* passes Gosberton, near Spalding, with a train of Railhead Treatment Trains vehicles heading for use in East Anglia on September 9 2014. *Pip Dunn*

*Bottom:* 37401 *Mary Queen of Scots* leads the 1156 Carlisle-Lancaster, away from Barrow on August 1 2015. *Anthony Hicks*

*Rear Cover top:* Preserved Class 35 Hymek D7017 stands at Dereham on 9 September 2017, with Class 20s D8188 and D8059 alongside. *Pip Dunn*

*Middle:* Colas Rail Freight's 37116 passes Spalding on February 4 2017 on the rear of a Peterborough to Doncaster test train. *Pip Dunn*

*Bottom:* GB Railfreight's 73968/966 pause at Rannoch on July 27 2016 with the 1950 Fort William-Edinburgh Caledonian Sleeper train. *Pip Dunn*

# Contents

# Introduction

Books which list the diesel and electric locos that have run on the National Rail network seem to fall into two categories; big weighty tomes with lots of information, or small pocket books that list just what is in traffic today.

Both have their advantage and also their limitations. This new book aims to bridge the gap and offer a handy, transportable book which allows the reader to 'tick off' everything they have seen, photographed, or travelled behind.

Technically, there are a lot of grey areas in how we classify a loco's status and often these lines are blurred. However I have tried, as best as I can, to draw up distinct areas, hence this book is split into four sections. They are:

**Section 1** which lists all the diesel and electric locomotives that are registered to run on the National Network rail system, as well as those locos which are in store or withdrawn but owned or 'operated' by franchised or open access train operating companies. Even here there are some anomalies, mainly on shunting locos which may, or may not, be allowed out of the confines of

HNRC's 20107 and 20096 are usually found on hire to GB Railfreight but on 17 September 2011 they were guests at the North Yorkshire Moors Railway and work the 1300 Pickering-Grosmont past Thomason Foss. *Anthony Hicks*

the depots or yards that they work at. Locos owned by spot hire companies and third parties, but used by franchised TOCs/FOCs are listed in this section.

These locos will have details of the key differences which affect the work they can undertake. Also listed is their TOPS Sector code as of 23 October 2017, their livery, owner and name if appropriate. Old numbers – pre-1973 D/E numbers and all previous TOPS numbers are also listed.

Locos owned by preservation groups that are main line registered are listed in this section. Some locos may – presently – not be fully main line compliant (such as missing Global System for Mobile Communications – Railway equipment - GSM-R) or be a shunting locomotive without a Train Protection Warning System (TPWS) but if they are used by a TOC then they are listed in this section. Not all locos in section 1 and 2 are on TOPS and have a pool code.

**Section 2** lists all locos that are owned by spot hire companies but not main line registered or not on hire to FOCs/TOCs. These may be in industrial use or have been redeployed/sold for use abroad, again relevant details are included. While these locos do not have current full main line registration, that could change.

Also included in this section are locos which have restricted NR registration – such as 25278 which can run between Middlesbrough and Whitby only.

It details all ex-BR and ex-TOC/FOC locomotives that have been sold for private use or pending disposal. Also included in this section are any locos which have been sold to scrap merchants but had not yet been broken up, as these could be sold on for reuse.

Finally, those locos moved abroad by the likes of DB Cargo or Freightliner, or sold for use by European operators, are also included here.

**Section 3** details all locos classed as 'preserved', regardless if they have been restored or not. This includes locos which may never have run, or realistically are unlikely to ever run again. It does *not* include locos located at heritage sites which are owned by FOCs or Spot hire companies; these are listed in Section 2.

Finally **Section 4** lists all ex-BR locos that have been disposed of – and so no longer physically exist. These are listed in class order with their final number, and all previous numbers are also listed. However, their names are not included nor are their detail differences and their disposal details.

Three-character owner and livery codes, sector codes and depot allocations are all listed in the appendices. Standard TOPS pool codes are used, but two-digit codes for depots and other locations are also listed.

Locos can, and of course will, change owner or status and so their inclusion in a certain section may change as events overtake them.

The information in this book is given in good faith and as far as is known, correct to 23 October 2017. Any corrections, input or comments should be sent to the author via the publisher.

Pip Dunn, Spalding, October 2017

# Codes for key loco detail differences

These are the key differences that affect the work or area that a loco can undertake. They are given by codes:

a Train air brakes only
b Operational steam heat boiler fitted
c Tripcocks fitted
d Dellner coupler fitted
e Operational Electric Train Supply
f Fire suppressant equipment fitted
g ERTMS equipment fitted
h Lickey banker auto coupler fitted
i Non-operational steam heat boiler retained
j Buffers fitted – where non standard
l Scharfenberg coupler fitted
k Engine stop-start equipment fitted
m Multiple Working equipment fitted – where non standard
n Multiple Working equipment removed – where non standard
o No train heating capability
p Snowplough brackets fitted (* main line loco fitted with snowploughs)
q Remote monitoring equipment fitted
r In-cab Radio Electronic Token Block (RETB) signalling fitted
s Slow speed control fitted
t Additional fuel tanks fitted
u Push-pull fitted
v Vacuum train brakes only
w Waist level duplicate brake pipes fitted
x Dual train brakes
y Non-operational Electric Train Supply
z Through Electric Train Supply wiring (loco is 'no heat')

All locos in sections 1 and 2 are deemed to be operational unless stated. All fittings relate to the loco at the time of press.

(S) Loco is in store in a serviceable condition. The loco may not have run for some time but could be returned to traffic relatively quickly. It may be stored pending an upgrade to meet group standards or may have been stopped to temporarily donate parts to another vehicle.

(U) Loco is in store in an unserviceable condition; the loco has been damaged, stripped, or laid up for a long period and would require major expenditure to return it to traffic. It may currently not meet group standards. Some of these locos may be for sale.

For preserved locos they are either classed as operational (OP), actively under restoration (UR) or stored for parts donation, disposal or restoration to start at a later date (UR). Locos on static display are also listed as SU. D5910 is classed as UC – under construction.

# Key abbreviations

| | |
|---|---|
| AC | Alternating current |
| DC | Direct current |
| ETH | Electric Train Heat |
| ETS | Electric Train Supply |
| ft | foot |
| gal | gallon |
| GSM-R | Global System for Mobile Communications – Railway |
| hp | Horsepower |
| in | inch |
| kN | Kilonewton |
| kV | kilovolt |
| kW | kilowatt |
| km/h | kilometres per hour |
| lbf | pounds force |
| lit | litre |
| m | metre |
| mph | miles per hour |
| OTMR | On Train Monitoring and Recording ('black box') |
| TPWS | Train Protection and Warning System |
| V | Volt |

# 1 The main line fleet

Locos are listed by the current TOPS numbers, their previous numbers – including pre-TOPS D numbers, fittings, the sector the loco is allocated to, the owner, livery, depot allocation or location the loco is at, and its current name.

Locos which had 89xxx numbers do NOT have these listed as they are not usually displayed other than in the cabs.

## Class 08

*Part of the mass order for the Standard BR 0-6-0 diesel electric shunter, of which over 1,000 were built from 1952, just a handful survive with a few train operators. More locos are owned by spot hire companies and are listed in section 2.*

| | |
|---|---|
| Built by: | BR Derby, Crewe, Darlington, Horwich |
| Years introduced: | 1952-62 |
| Wheel arrangement: | 0-6-0 |
| Weight: | 49-50 tons |
| Length: | 29ft 3in (8.91m) |
| Engine Type: | English Electric 6KT |
| Engine output: | 400hp (298kW) |
| Power at rail: | 260hp (194kW) |
| Tractive effort: | 35,000lbf (156kN) |
| Continuous tractive effort: | 11,100lbf (49kN) |
| Maximum design speed: | 15-20mph (25-33km/h) |
| Brake Force: | 19 tonnes |
| Route Availability: | 5 |
| Main generator type: | EE801-8E or E801-14E |
| Auxiliary generator type: | EE736-2D, EE736-4E or EE906-3D |
| Traction Motor type: | EE506-6A or EE506-7C |
| Fuel tank capacity: | 668gal (3,036lit) |
| Multiple working type: | not fitted |

East Midlands Trains' 08690 *DAVID THIRKILL* at Neville Hill depot. This is one of four Class 08s based here. *Pip Dunn.*

| Loco's current TOPS number | Previous official numbers carried | Key detail differences | Current TOPS Sector | Vehicle Owner | Current Livery | Current depot allocation or location | Current name (as displayed on the loco) Minor wording on crests, plaques or graphics is excluded |
|---|---|---|---|---|---|---|---|
| 08410 | D3525 | ao | EFSH | GWR | GWR | PZ | |
| 08411 | D3526 | ao | MBDL | RSS | BRW | WI (U) | |
| 08417 | D3532 | ao | QADD | NET | NRY | DF (S) | |
| 08418 | D3533 | ao | AWCA | WCR | EWS | CS | |
| 08451 | D3566 | ao | ATZZ | ALS | BRW | LO | *MA SMITH* |
| 08454 | D3569 | aod | ATLO | ALS | BRW | WD | |
| 08472 | D3587 | ao | RFSH | WAB | BLK | EC | |
| 08480 | D3595 | ao | MBDL | RSS | RSS | NC | |
| 08483 | D3598 | ao | EFSH | GWR | BLK | OO | *NEIL / SCOUSEY Neil Morgan 1964-2014 Team Leader OOC* |
| 08485 | D3600 | ao | AWCA | WCR | BRW | CS | |
| 08507 | D3662 | ao | RTSO | RIV | OXB | CD | |
| 08511 | D3673 | ao | MBDL | RSS | RSS | CM | |
| 08523 | D3685 | ao | MRSO | RMS | RMS | IS | |
| 08525 | D3687 | ao | EMSL | EMT | EMB | NL | *DUNCAN BEDFORD* |
| 08530 | D3692 | ao | DDIN | POR | FLR | SM | |
| 08531 | D3693 | ao | DDIN | POR | FPH | WD | |
| 08571 | D3738 | ao | HBSH | WAB | BLK | FX | |
| 08575 | D3742 | xo | DHLT | POR | FLR | LH (U) | |
| 08585 | D3752 | ao | DDIN | POR | FLR | TP | *Vicky* |
| 08588 | D3755 | ao | MRSO | RMS | RMS | DF | |
| 08596 | D3763 | ao | HBSH | WAB | BLK | EC | |
| 08611 | D3778 | ao | ATLO | ALS | BRW | WB | |
| 08616 | D3783 | xo | EJLO | LON | LON | TS | *TYSELEY 100* |
| 08617 | D3784 | aod | ATLO | ALS | BLK | OX | *Steve Purser* |
| 08624 | D3791 | xo | DDIN | POR | FPH | SM | *Rambo Paul Ramsey* |
| 08631 | D3798 | xo | MBDL | LSL | BRW | CD | |
| 08641 | D3808 | ao | EFSH | GWR | BRW | LA | *LAIRA* |
| 08644 | D3811 | ao | EFSH | GWR | BRW | LA | *Laira Diesel Depot 50 Years 1962-2012* |
| 08645 | D3812 | ao | EFSH | GWR | DEP | LA | *Mike Baggott* |
| 08663 | D3830 | ao | EFSH | GWR | BRW | PM | *St Silas* |
| 08670 | D3837 | ao | MBDL | RSS | RSS | BN | |
| 08678 | D3845 | ao | AWCX | WCR | GLA | CS (U) | *Artila* |
| 08683 | D3850 | ao | MBDL | RSS | EWS | NC | |
| 08690 | D3857 | ao | EMSL | EMT | EMB | NL | *DAVID THIRKILL* |
| 08691 | D3858 | xo | DDIN | FLI | FLG | FX | *Terri* |
| 08696 | D3863 | ao | ATLO | ALS | BRW | WB | |
| 08704 | D3871 | ao | RTSO | LSL | OXB | BU | |
| 08721 | D3889 | ao | ATLO | ALS | BRW | WD | *Longsight TMD* |
| 08735 | D3903 | ao | WQDA | DBC | EWS | EH (U) | |
| 08737 | D3905 | ao | | LSL | EWS | CD | |
| 08780 | D3948 | xo | MBDL | LSL | BLE | SH | |
| 08785 | D3953 | ao | DDIN | POR | FLR | LH | |
| 08790 | D3958 | ao | ATLO | ALS | BRW | ZG (U) | |
| 08795 | D3963 | ao | EFSH | GWR | BLK | LE | *Landore* |
| 08805 | D3973 | xo | EJLO | LON | RSR | SI | |
| 08822 | D3990 | ao | EFSH | GWR | ICS | PM | *Dave Mills* |
| 08836 | D4004 | ao | EFSH | GWR | GWR | OO | |
| 08887 | D4117 | ao | DDIN | ALS | BRW | ZG (U) | |
| 08891 | D4121 | ao | DHLT | POR | FLR | ZG (U) | |
| 08899 | D4129 | xo | EMSL | EMT | MID | DY | *Midland Counties Railway 175 Years 1839-2014* |

| | | | | | | | |
|---|---|---|---|---|---|---|---|
| 08908 | D4138 | ao | EMSL | EMT | EMB | NL | *IVAN STEPHENSON* |
| 08925 | D4155 | ao | GBWM | GBR | GWS | WG | |
| 08934 | D4164 | ao | GBWM | GBR | GWS | DG | |
| 08948 | D4178 | aol | GPSS | EUK | EUK | TI | |
| 08950 | D4180 | ao | EMSL | EMT | EMB | NL | *DAVID LIGHTFOOT* |

Note: 08451/795 have buckeye couplers

Note: 08735 has a swinghead coupler and remote control equipment

Note: Not all Class 08/09s are passed to run on the main line and may be restricted to designated areas. TOCs which hire shunting locomotives may have these vehicles swapped occasionally with those listed in section 2.

## Class 09

*Another version of the BR standard shunter the Class 09s with a higher top speed. 26 were originally built, but 12 were later converted by BR from Class 08s.*

| | |
|---|---|
| Built by: | BR Darlington, Horwich |
| Years introduced: | 1959-62 |
| Wheel arrangement: | 0-6-0 |
| Weight: | 49 tons |
| Length: | 29ft 3in (8.91m) |
| Engine Type: | English Electric 6KT |
| Engine output: | 400hp (298kW) |
| Power at rail: | 260hp (194kW) |
| Tractive effort: | 25,000lbf (111kN) |
| Continuous tractive effort: | 8,800lbf (39kN) |
| Maximum design speed: | 27mph (34km/h) |
| Brake Force: | 19 tonnes |
| Route Availability: | 5 |
| Main generator type: | EE801-8E or E801-14E |
| Auxiliary generator type: | EE906-3D |
| Traction Motor type: | EE506-10C |
| Fuel tank capacity: | 668gal (3,036lit) |
| Multiple Working type: | Not fitted |

| | | | | | | |
|---|---|---|---|---|---|---|
| 09002 | D3666 | ao | GBWM | GBR | GWS | WG |
| 09007 | D3671 | aow | | LOL | GWS | WN |
| 09009 | D3720 | ao | GBWM | GBR | GWS | DL |

GBRf Class 20, 20901 at Sheffield Park during a visit to the Bluebell Railway in April 2016. The loco sports three-piece miniature snowploughs. *Pip Dunn*

## Class 20

*An initial 20 English Electric Type 1s were part of the 1955 Pilot Scheme leading to a further 208 being built between 1957-68. A handful remain in use on the main line.*

| | |
|---|---|
| Built by: | English Electric Vulcan Foundry or Robert Stephenson & Hawthorns |
| Years introduced: | 1957-68 |
| Wheel arrangement: | Bo-Bo |
| Weight: | 73 tons |
| Length: | 46ft 9in (14.26m) |
| Engine Type: | English Electric 8SVT Mk 2 |
| Engine output: | 1,000hp (746kW) |
| Power at rail: | 770hp (574kW) |
| Tractive effort: | 42,000lbf (187kN) |
| Continuous tractive effort: | 25,000lbf (111kN) |
| Maximum design speed: | 75mph (120km/h) |
| Brake Force: | 35 tons |
| Route Availability: | 5 |
| Main generator type: | EE819-3C |
| Auxiliary generator type: | EE911-2B |
| Traction Motor type: | EE526/5D (20007), 526/8D (others) |
| Fuel tank capacity: | 380gal (1,727lit) |
| Multiple Working type: | Blue Star |

## Class 20/0 – standard locos

| | | | | | | | |
|---|---|---|---|---|---|---|---|
| 20007 | D8007 | ao | MOLO | MOW | GYP | SK (U) | |
| 20096 | D8096 | aocp | GBEE | HNR | BRB | BH | *Ian Goddard 1938-2016* |
| 20107 | D8107 | aocp | GBEE | HNR | BRB | BH | |
| 20118 | D8118 | aop* | GBEE | HNR | RSR | BH | *Saltburn-by-the-Sea* |
| 20132 | D8132 | aop* | GBEE | HNR | RSR | BH | *Barrow Hill Depot* |
| 20142 | D8142 | xocp | MOLO | MOW | MRM | SK | *SIR JOHN BETJEMAN* |
| 20189 | D8189 | xop | MOLO | MOW | BRB | SK | |
| 20205 | D8305 | aop | MOLO | MOW | BRB | SK | |
| 20227 | D8327 | xop | MOLO | CTL | MRM | SK | |

## Class 20/3 – refurbished locos

Details as per Class 20/0

| | |
|---|---|
| Route Availability: | 5 (20301-305), 6 – 20308-314 |
| Traction Motor type: | EE526/5D (20301/312), 526/8D (others) |
| Fuel tank capacity: | 640gal (2,909lit, 20301-305), 1,090gal (4,909lit, 20306-315), |
| Multiple Working type: | DRS system |

| | | | | | | | |
|---|---|---|---|---|---|---|---|
| 20301 | 20047, D8047 | aotp | XHSS | DRS | DRC | BH (U) | |
| 20302 | 20084, D8084 | aotp | XHNC | DRS | DRC | KM | |
| 20303 | 20127, D8127 | aotp | XHNC | DRS | DRC | KM | *Max Joule 1958-1999* |
| 20304 | 20120, D8120 | aotp | XHSS | DRS | DRC | BH (U) | |
| 20305 | 20095, D8095 | aotp | XHNC | DRS | DRC | KM | *Class 20 'Fifty'* |
| 20308 | 20187, D8187 | aotp | XHSS | DRS | DRC | BH (U) | |
| 20309 | 20075,D8075 | aotp | XHSS | DRS | DRC | BH (U) | |
| 20311 | 20102, D8102 | aotcp | GBEE | HNR | HNO | BH | |
| 20312 | 20042, D8042 | aotp | XHNC | DRS | DRC | KM | |
| 20314 | 20117, D8117 | aotcp | GBEE | HNR | HNO | BH | |

## Class 20/9 – former Hunslet Barclay locos

Details as per Class 20/0

Traction Motor type: 526/8D

| | | | | | | |
|---|---|---|---|---|---|---|
| 20901 | 20101, D8101 | aotcp | GBEE | HNR | GBR | BH |
| 20905 | 20225, D8325 | aotcp | GBEE | HNR | GBR | BH |

## Class 31

*A derivative of an initial 20-strong order for the 1955 Pilot Scheme – the fleet eventually totalled 263 locos. All were originally fitted with Mirrlees engines but these proved unreliable and were replaced by EE engines in 1964-69. The pilot scheme locos were all withdrawn by 1980, and 70 locos were later converted to have ETH. A handful remain in use on the main line.*

| | |
|---|---|
| Built by: | Brush Ltd, Loughborough |
| Years introduced: | 1964-69 (converted from Class 30s) |
| Wheel arrangement: | A1A-A1A |
| Weight: | 107-111 tons |
| Length: | 56ft 9in (17.29m) |
| Engine Type: | English Electric 12SVT |
| Engine output: | 1,470hp (1,097kW) |
| Power at rail: | 1,170hp (872kW) |
| Tractive effort: | 35,900lbf (160kN) |
| Continuous tractive effort: | 18,700lbf (83kN) |
| Maximum design speed: | 90mph (144km/h) |
| Brake Force: | 49 tons |
| Route Availability: | 5 |
| Main generator type: | Brush TG160-48 |
| Auxiliary generator type: | Brush TG69-42 |
| Traction Motor type: | Brush TM73-68 |
| Fuel tank capacity: | 530gal (2,385lit) |
| Multiple Working type: | Blue Star |

## Class 31/1 – standard locos

| | | | | | | |
|---|---|---|---|---|---|---|
| 31105 | D5523 | ao | QADD | NET | NRY | DF (S) |
| 31190 | D5613 | xop | HTLX | DCR | GYP | WH (U) |
| 31233 | D5660 | ao | QADD | NET | NRY | DF (S) |

31233 has additional spotlights and recording cameras fitted at No. 2 end

## Class 31/4 – locos fitted with ETH

Details as per Class 31/1 except:

| | |
|---|---|
| ETH generator type: | Brush BL100-30 |
| ETH index: | 66 |
| Route Availability: | 6 |

| | | | | | | |
|---|---|---|---|---|---|---|
| 31452 | D5809, 31279, 31552 | xef | HTLX | DCR | DCG | WH |
| 31454 | D5654, 31228, 31554 | xef | HTLX | DCR | ICM | WH (U) |
| 31468 | D5855, 31321, 31568 | xef | MRLO | DCR | FRG | WO (U) |

Currently the only Class 31 operating on the main line is DC Rail's 31452, seen at Kidderminster in May 2016. The loco sports unbranded Devon & Cornwall Railways green livery. Pip Dunn.

## Class 31/6 – fitted with through ETH wiring

Details as per Class 31/1.

| | | | | | | |
|---|---|---|---|---|---|---|
| 31601 | D5609, 31186 | xozf | HTLX | DCR | DCR | WH (U) |
| 31602 | D5614, 31191 | xozf | HTLX | DCR | NRY | WO (U) |

Class 33/1 D6515 *Lt Jenny Lewis RN* is owned by the 71A Loco group but is main line registered and has seen use on Swanage-Wareham shuttles. It passes Norden on 21 June 2017 with the 1423 Swanage-Wareham. *Anthony Hicks*

## Class 33

*Type 3 design built by BRCW for the Southern Region, fitted with dual brakes and electric train heat from new. 19 locos were converted to push pull operation (Class 33/1s) and the final 12 were built with a narrower body profile for working on the gauge-restricted Hastings line (Class 33/2).*

| | |
|---|---|
| Built by: | Birmingham RC&W |
| Years introduced: | 1960-62 |
| Wheel arrangement: | Bo-Bo |
| Weight: | 77 tons |
| Length: | 50ft 9in (15.47m) |
| Engine Type: | Sulzer 8LDA28A |
| Engine output: | 1,550hp (1,154kW) |
| Power at rail: | 1,215hp (906kW) |
| Tractive effort: | 45,000lbf (200kN) |
| Continuous tractive effort: | 26,000lbf (116kN) |
| ETH generator type: | Crompton Parkinson CAG392-A1 |
| ETH index: | 48 |
| Maximum design speed: | 85mph (137km/h) |
| Brake Force: | 35 tons |
| Route Availability: | 6 |
| Main generator type: | Crompton Parkinson CAG391-B1 |
| Auxiliary generator type: | Crompton Parkinson CAG193-A1 |
| Traction Motor type: | Crompton Parkinson C171-C2 |
| Fuel tank capacity: | 750gal (3,410lit) |
| Multiple Working type: | Blue Star |

## Class 33/0 – standard locos

| | | | | | | | |
|---|---|---|---|---|---|---|---|
| 33012 | D6515 | xep | MBDL | SOA | GYP | SR | *Lt Jenny Lewis RN* |
| 33025 | D6543 | xyp* | AWCA | WCR | WCR | CS | |
| 33029 | D6547 | aop* | AWCX | WCR | WCR | CS (U) | |
| 33030 | D6548 | ayp | AWCX | WCR | DRU | CS (U) | |

## Class 33/2 – narrow 'Hastings gauge' body

| | | | | | | | |
|---|---|---|---|---|---|---|---|
| 33207 | D6592 | aop* | AWCA | WCR | WCR | CS | *Jim Martin* |

## Class 37

*Standard Diesel Electric Type 3 design, of which 309 were built. 135 locos were refurbished in the late 1980s, including 31 with ETH (Class 37/4), 44 with added ballast weights (Class 37/7) and six with test bed alternative engines (Class 37/9). 12 locos were later converted with through ETH wiring for Eurostar.*

| | |
|---|---|
| Built by: | English Electric, Vulcan Foundry or Robert Stephenson & Hawthorns |
| Years introduced: | 1960-65 |
| Wheel arrangement: | Co-Co |
| Weight: | 102-108 tons |
| Length: | 61ft 6in (18.74m) |
| Engine Type: | English Electric 12CSVT |
| Engine output: | 1,750hp (1,304kW) |
| Power at rail: | 1,250hp (932kW) |
| Tractive effort: | 55,500lbf (247kN) |
| Continuous tractive effort: | 35,000lbf (156kN) |
| Maximum design speed: | 90mph (144km/h) |
| Brake Force: | 50 tons |
| Route Availability: | 5 |
| Main generator type: | EE822-10G, EE822-13G or EE822-16J |
| Auxiliary generator type: | EE911/5C |
| Traction Motor type: | EE538-1A or EE538-5A |
| Fuel tank capacity: | 890gal (4,046lit) or t – 1,690gal (7,682lit) |
| Multiple Working type: | Blue Star (DRS system: 37038/059/069/218/259) |

## Class 37/0 – standard locos

| | | | | | | | |
|---|---|---|---|---|---|---|---|
| 37025 | D6725 | xbprz* | COTS | STG | BLL | BH | *Inverness TMD* |
| 37038 | D6738 | aot | XHNC | DRS | DRN | KM | |
| 37057 | D6757 | xi | COTS | COL | GYP | BH | |
| 37059 | D6759 | aotr | XHNC | DRS | DRN | KM | |
| 37069 | D6769 | aotr | XHNC | DRS | DRN | KM | |
| 37099 | D6799, 37324 | xirp* | COTS | COL | COL | BH (U) | *MERL EVANS 1947-2016* |
| 37116 | D6816 | xor | COTS | COL | COL | BH | |
| 37146 | D6846 | xot | COLS | COL | CCE | BH (U) | |
| 37165 | D6865, 37374 | xot | | WCR | CCT | CS (U) | |
| 37175 | D6875 | xorp* | COTS | COL | COL | BH | |
| 37188 | D6888 | xip | COLS | COL | UND | BH (U) | |
| 37207 | D6907 | aotp | COLS | COL | BRB | BH (U) | |
| 37218 | D6918 | aotrp* | XHNC | DRS | DRN | KM | |
| 37219 | D6919 | aotrp* | COTS | COL | COL | BH | *Jonty Jarvis 8-12-1998 to 18-3-2005* |

Colas Rail Freight's 37057, in British Railways green, heads north from Spalding on the rear of a test train on 15 October 2016. *Pip Dunn*

| | | | | | | | |
|---|---|---|---|---|---|---|---|
| 37254 | D6954 | aotrp | COTS | COL | COL | BH | *Cardiff Canton* |
| 37259 | D6959, 37380 | aotrp* | XHNC | DRS | DRC | KM | |

Note: 37219 has monitoring equipment mounting brackets fitted at No. 2 end

## Class 37/4 – refurbished locos with ETH

Details as per 37/0 except:

| | |
|---|---|
| Converted by: | BREL Crewe |
| Years introduced: | 1985/86 |
| Tractive effort: | 57,440lbf (256kN) |
| Continuous tractive effort: | 41,250lbf (184kN) |
| ETH alternator type: | Brush BAH701 |
| ETH index: | 30 |
| Design speed: | 80mph (128km/h) |
| Main alternator type: | Brush BA1005A |
| Auxiliary alternator type: | Brush BA606A |
| Multiple Working type: | Blue Star (DRS system and Blue Star: 37423) |

DRS's 37419 *Carl Haviland* stands at Lowestoft on 7 April 2017 with the 1548 Greater Anglia train for Norwich. 37425 *Concrete Bob/Sir Robert McAlpine* is on the rear. *Pip Dunn*

| | | | | | | | |
|---|---|---|---|---|---|---|---|
| 37401 | D6968, 37268 | aetp* | XHAC | DRS | BLL | KM | *Mary Queen of Scots* |
| 37402 | D6974, 37274 | aetp* | XHAC | DRS | BLL | KM | *Stephen Middlemore 23.12.1954 – 8.6.2013* |
| 37403 | D6607, 37307 | xetfp* | XHAC | SRP | BLL | KM | *Isle of Mull* |
| 37405 | D6982, 37282 | aerftp* | XHAC | DRS | DRC | KM | |
| 37407 | D6605, 37305 | aetfp* | XHSS | DRS | BLL | DF (U) | |
| 37409 | D6970, 37270 | aetfp* | XHSS | DRS | DRC | DF (S) | *Lord Hinton* |
| 37418 | D6971, 37271 | xetp* | MBDL | BEN | BLU | BH (U) | |
| 37419 | D6991, 37291 | aerftp* | XHAC | DRS | DRC | KM | *Carl Haviland 1954-2012* |
| 37421 | D6967, 37267 | aetfp* | COTS | COL | COL | BH | |
| 37422 | D6966, 37266 | aerftp* | XHAC | DRS | DRU | KM | |
| 37423 | D6996, 37296 | aerftp* | XHAC | DRS | DRX | KM | *Spirit of the Lakes* |
| 37424 | D6979, 37279 | aetfp* | XHAC | DRS | BLL | KM | *Avro Vulcan XH558* |
| 37425 | D6992, 37292 | aerftp* | XHAC | DRS | DRC | KM | *Sir Robert McAlpine / Concrete Bob* |

Note: 37424 carries the numbers 37558 on its bodysides

## Class 37/5 – refurbished locos with no heating

Details as per Class 37/4 except:

Years introduced: 1985-89
Tractive effort: 55,590lbf (248kN)
Multiple Working type: Blue Star (DRS system and Blue Star: 37667/688)
No train heating

| | | | | | | | |
|---|---|---|---|---|---|---|---|
| 37516 | D6786, 37086 | xotrp* | AWCA | WCR | WCR | CS | *Loch Laidon* |
| 37517 | D6718, 37018 | xotp | AWCX | WCR | LHO | CS (U) | |
| 37518 | D6776, 37076 | xotrp* | AWCA | WCR | WCR | CS | |

## Class 37/6 – refurbished former Eurostar locos

Details as per Class 37/5 except:

| | |
|---|---|
| Years introduced: | 1995-96 |
| Design speed: | 90mph (144km/h) |
| Multiple Working type: | Blue Star (DRS system: 37602/605-611,<br>DRS system and Blue Star: 37601/603/604)<br>Originally modified with through ETH wiring |

| | | | | | | | |
|---|---|---|---|---|---|---|---|
| 37601 | D6705, 37005, 37501 | aotdrp* | GROG | ROG | EPX | LR | *Perseus* |
| 37602 | D6782, 37082, 37502 | aotrzp* | XHNC | DRS | DRC | KM | |
| 37603 | D6739, 37039, 37604 | aotp | XHSS | DRS | DRC | DF (S) | |
| 37604 | D6707, 37007, 37506 | aotp | XHCC | DRS | DRC | KM | |
| 37605 | D6736, 37036, 37507 | aotrp | XHNC | DRS | DRC | KM | |
| 37606 | D6790, 37090, 37508 | aotp* | XHNC | DRS | DRC | KM | |
| 37607 | D6803, 37103, 37511 | aotp | XHRL | COL | DRU | BH | |
| 37608 | D6722, 37022, 37512 | aotrp* | GROG | EPX | EPX | LR | *Andromeda* |
| 37609 | D6815, 37115, 37514 | aotrp* | XHNC | DRS | DRN | KM | |
| 37610 | D6871, 37171, 37687 | aotrp | MBDL | LSL | BLB | CD (S) | |
| 37611 | D6881, 37181, 37690 | aotrp* | EPUK | EPX | EPX | LR | *Pegasus* |

## Class 37/5 (continued)

| | | | | | | | |
|---|---|---|---|---|---|---|---|
| 37667 | D6851, 37151 | aotrp | MBDL | LSL | DRU | CD (S) | |
| 37668 | D6957, 37257 | xotrp | AWCA | WCR | WCR | CS | |
| 37669 | D6829, 37129 | xotrp | AWCA | WCR | WCR | CS | |
| 37676 | D6826, 37126 | xotp | AWCA | WCR | WCR | CS (U) | *Loch Rannoch* |
| 37685 | D6934, 37234 | xotrp* | AWCA | WCR | WCR | CS | *Loch Arkaig* |

## Class 37/7 – refurbished locos with ballast weights

Details as per Class 37/5 except:

| | |
|---|---|
| Years introduced: | 1986-88 |
| Weight: | 120 tons |
| Tractive effort | 62,000lbf (276kN) |
| Brake Force: | 60 tons |
| Route Availability: | 7 |
| Multiple Working type: | Blue Star (DRS system and Blue Star: 37716) |

| | | | | | | |
|---|---|---|---|---|---|---|
| 37706 | D6716, 37016 | xotrp* | AWCA | WCR | WCR | CS |
| 37710 | D6744, 37044 | xotp | | WCR | LHO | CS (U) |
| 37712 | D6802, 37102 | xotp | AWCX | WCR | WCR | CS (U) |
| 37716 | D6794, 37094 | aotfp* | XHNC | DRS | DRN | KM |
| 37800 | D6843, 37143 | aotdp* | EPUK | EPX | EPX | LR |
| 37884 | D6883, 37183 | aotp | EPUK | EPX | EPX | LR |

Note: 37884 has a tightlock coupler fitted

## Class 37/9 – refurbished locos with trial engines

Details as per Class 37/7 except:

| | |
|---|---|
| Year introduced: | 1986 |
| Engine Type: | 37901-904 – Mirrlees MB275T |
| | 37905-906 – Ruston RK270T |
| Engine output: | 1,800hp (1,340kW) – 37901-906 |
| Power at rail: | 1,300hp (940kW) – 37901-906 |
| Tractive effort | 62,680lbf (279kN) |
| Multiple Working type: | Blue Star |

| | | | | | | |
|---|---|---|---|---|---|---|
| 37901 | D6850, 37150 | xotp | COTS | COL | RFO | SE (U) |
| 37905 | D6836, 37136 | xotp | UKRM | UKR | GYP | LR (S) |
| 37906 | D6906, 37206 | xotp | UKRM | UKR | RFO | LR (S) |

## Class 97 – Network Rail Class 37/0s with ERTMS

Details as per Class 37/0 except:

| | |
|---|---|
| Years introduced: | 2008 |
| Multiple Working type: | Blue Star |

| | | | | | | | |
|---|---|---|---|---|---|---|---|
| 97301 | D6800, 37100 | xotgp | QETS | NET | NRY | ZA | |
| 97302 | D6870, 37170 | xotgp* | QETS | NET | NRY | ZA | |
| 97303 | D6878, 37178 | xotgp* | QETS | NET | NRY | ZA | |
| 97304 | D6917, 37217 | xotgp | QETS | NET | NRY | ZA | *John Tiley* |

40145 is the only main line registered Class 40. The loco passes Ruswarp on with the 0840 Pickering-Whitby on 21 April 2007 while visiting the North Yorkshire Moors Railway for a diesel event. *Anthony Hicks*

## Class 40

*A pilot scheme of ten locos led to another 190 locos being ordered. All were withdrawn by 1985 bar the pioneer loco D200 (40122) which was retained for special duties until withdrawal in 1988. 40145 returned to the main line in 2002.*

| | |
|---|---|
| Built by: | English Electric, Vulcan Foundry |
| Years introduced: | 1958-62 |
| Wheel arrangement: | 1Co-Co1 |
| Length: | 69ft 6in (21.18m) |
| Weight: | 136 tons |
| Engine Type: | English Electric 16SVT Mk 2 |
| Engine output: | 2,000hp (1,492kW) |
| Power at rail: | 1,550hp (1,156kW) |
| Tractive effort: | 52,000lb |
| Continuous tractive effort: | 30,900lbf (137kN) |
| Maximum design speed: | 90mph (144km/h) |
| Brake Force: | 51 tons |
| Route Availability: | 6 |
| Main generator type: | EE822 |
| Auxiliary generator type: | EE911-2B |
| Traction Motor type: | EE 526-5D |
| Fuel tank capacity: | 710gal (3,195lit) |
| Multiple Working type: | Blue Star |

| | | | | | | | |
|---|---|---|---|---|---|---|---|
| 40145 | D345 | | XO | CFSL | CFP | BRB | BQ |

## Class 43

*The HST power cars (not to be confused with the Class 43 North British Warship Diesel hydraulics), run in pairs, either end of a rake of Mk 3 trailer vehicles. All were built with Paxman Valenta engines but all have now been re-engined with either MTU or VP185 engines. Just three have been written off after collisions. The Virgin East Coast and some Great Western Railway power cars will be replaced by Class 800/801/802 multiple units in the next three years. 54 power cars are destined for ScotRail and the transfers of the first locos has started.*

| | |
|---|---|
| Built by: | BREL Crewe |
| Years introduced: | 1976-82 |
| Wheel arrangement: | Bo-Bo |
| Weight: | 70 tons |
| Length: | 58ft 5in (17.80m) |
| Original engine: | Paxman Valenta 12RP200L (all since removed) |
| Replacement engines: | Mirrlees Blackstone MB190 (all since removed) |
| | Paxman 12VP185 (EMPC locos only) |
| | MTU16V4000 R41R |
| Engine output: | 2,700hp (2,010kW) |
| Power at rail: | 1,770hp (1,320kW) |
| Tractive effort: | 17,980lbf (80kN) |
| Continuous Tractive effort: | 10,340lbf (46kN) |
| Maximum design speed: | 125mph (200km/h) |
| Brake force | 35t |
| Route Availability: | 6 |
| Main alternator type: | Brush BA1001B (VP185 locos), Brush BA1001C (MTU locos) |

Traction Motor type: 43002-123/153-198 (Brush TMH68-46), 43124-152 (GECG417AZ)
Fuel tank capacity: 1,030gal (4,680lit)
Multiple Working type: Within class only

| | | | | | | |
|---|---|---|---|---|---|---|
| 43002 | ae | EFPC | ANG | HST | LA | *Sir Kenneth Grange* |
| 43003 | ae | EFPC | ANG | FGB | LA | *ISAMBARD KINGDOM BRUNEL* |
| 43004 | ae | EFPC | ANG | FGB | LA | |
| 43005 | ae | EFPC | ANG | GWT | LA | |
| 43009 | ae | EFPC | ANG | FGB | LA | |
| 43010 | ae | EFPC | ANG | FGB | LA | |
| 43012 | ae | EFPC | ANG | FGB | LA | *Exeter Panel Signal Box 21st Anniversary 2009* |
| 43013 | aej | QCAR | POR | NRY | EC | |
| 43014 | aej | QCAR | POR | NRY | EC | *The Railway Observer* |
| 43015 | ae | EFPC | ANG | FGB | LA | |
| 43016 | ae | EFPC | ANG | GWT | LA | |
| 43017 | ae | EFPC | ANG | FGB | LA | *Hannahs discoverhannahs.org* |
| 43018 | ae | EFPC | ANG | FGB | LA | |
| 43020 | ae | EFPC | ANG | FGB | LA | *mtu Power Passion Partnership* |
| 43021 | ae | HAPC | ANG | FGU | EC | |
| 43022 | ae | EFPC | ANG | FGB | LA | *The Duke of Edinburgh's Award Diamond Anniversary 1956-2016* |
| 43023 | ae | EFPC | ANG | FGB | LA | *SQN LDR HAROLD STARR ONE OF THE FEW* |
| 43024 | ae | EFPC | ANG | FGB | LA | *Great Western Society 1961-2011 Didcot Railway Centre* |
| 43025 | ae | EFPC | ANG | FGB | LA | *INSTITUTION OF RAILWAY OPERATORS 2000-2010 TEN YEARS PROMOTING OPERATIONAL EXCELLENCE* |
| 43026 | ae | EFPC | ANG | FGB | LA | *Michael Eavis* |
| 43027 | ae | EFPC | ANG | FGS | LA | |
| 43028 | ae | EFPC | ANG | FGB | LA | |
| 43029 | ae | EFPC | ANG | FGB | LA | |
| 43030 | ae | EFPC | ANG | FGB | LA | *Christian Lewis Trust* |
| 43031 | ae | EFPC | ANG | FGB | LA | |
| 43032 | ae | EFPC | ANG | FGB | LA | |
| 43033 | ae | HAPC | ANG | FGU | EC | |
| 43034 | ae | EFPC | ANG | FGB | LA | *TravelWatch South West* |
| 43035 | ae | EFPC | ANG | FGB | LA | |
| 43036 | ae | HAPC | ANG | FGU | EC | |
| 43037 | ae | EFPC | ANG | FGB | LA | *PENYDARREN* |
| 43040 | ae | EFPC | ANG | FGB | LA | *Bristol St Philip's Marsh* |
| 43041 | ae | EFPC | ANG | GWT | LE | *Meningitis Trust Support for Life* |
| 43042 | ae | EFPC | ANG | FGB | LE | |
| 43043 | ae | EMPC | POR | EMB | NL | |
| 43044 | ae | EMPC | POR | EMB | NL | |
| 43045 | ae | EMPC | POR | EMB | NL | |
| 43046 | ae | EMPC | POR | EMB | NL | |
| 43047 | ae | EMPC | POR | EMB | NL | |
| 43048 | ae | EMPC | POR | EMB | NL | *TCB Miller MBE* |

| | | | | | | |
|---|---|---|---|---|---|---|
| 43049 | ae | EMPC | POR | EMB | NL | *Neville Hill* |
| 43050 | ae | EMPC | POR | EMB | NL | |
| 43052 | ae | EMPC | POR | EMB | NL | |
| 43053 | ae | EFPC | POR | FGB | LE | *University of Worcester* |
| 43054 | ae | EMPC | POR | EMB | NL | |
| 43055 | ae | EMPC | POR | EMB | NL | *The Sheffield Star 125 Years* |
| 43056 | ae | EFPC | POR | FGB | LE | *The Royal British Legion* |
| 43058 | ae | EMPC | POR | EMB | NL | |
| 43059 | ae | EMPC | POR | EMB | NL | |
| 43060 | ae | EMPC | POR | EMB | NL | |
| 43061 | ae | EMPC | POR | EMB | NL | *The Fearless Foxes* |
| 43062 | ae | QCAR | POR | NRY | EC | *John Armitt* |
| 43063 | ae | EFPC | POR | FGB | LE | |
| 43064 | ae | EMPC | POR | EMB | NL | |
| 43066 | ae | EMPC | POR | EMB | NL | |
| 43069 | ae | EFPC | POR | FGB | LE | |
| 43070 | ae | EFPC | POR | FGB | LE | *The Corps of Royal Electrical & Mechanical Engineers* |
| 43071 | ae | EFPC | POR | FGB | LE | |
| 43073 | ae | EMPC | POR | EMB | NL | |
| 43075 | ae | EMPC | POR | EMB | NL | |
| 43076 | ae | EMPC | POR | EMB | NL | *IN SUPPORT OF HELP FOR HEROES* |
| 43078 | ae | EFPC | POR | FGB | LE | |
| 43079 | ae | EFPC | POR | FGB | LE | |
| 43081 | ae | EMPC | POR | EMB | NL | |
| 43082 | ae | EMPC | POR | EMB | NL | *RAILWAY Children* |
| 43083 | ae | EMPC | POR | EMB | NL | |
| 43086 | ae | EFPC | POR | FGB | LE | |
| 43087 | ae | EFPC | POR | FGB | LE | *11 Explosive Ordnance Disposal Regiment Royal Logistics Corps* |
| 43088 | ae | EFPC | POR | FGB | LE | |
| 43089 | ae | EMPC | POR | EMB | NL | |
| 43091 | ae | EFPC | POR | FGB | LE | |
| 43092 | ae | EFPC | FIR | FGB | LE | |
| 43093 | ae | EFPC | FIR | GWA | LE | *Old Oak Common HST Depot 1976-2018* |
| 43094 | ae | EFPC | FIR | FGB | LE | |
| 43097 | ae | EFPC | FIR | FGB | LE | *Environment Agency* |
| 43098 | ae | EFPC | FIR | FGB | LE | |
| 43122 | ae | EFPC | FIR | FGB | LE | |
| 43124 | ae | EFPC | ANG | FGB | LE | |
| 43125 | ae | EFPC | ANG | FGB | LE | |
| 43126 | ae | EFPC | ANG | FGB | LE | |
| 43127 | ae | EFPC | ANG | FGB | LE | *Sir Peter Parker 1924-2002 Cotswold Line 150* |
| 43128 | ae | EFPC | ANG | FGB | LE | |
| 43129 | ae | EFPC | ANG | FGB | LE | |
| 43130 | ae | EFPC | ANG | FGB | LE | |
| 43131 | ae | EFPC | ANG | FGB | LE | |
| 43132 | ae | HAPC | ANG | FGU | EC | |
| 43133 | ae | EFPC | ANG | FGB | LE | |
| 43134 | ae | HAPC | ANG | FGU | EC | |
| 43135 | ae | EFPC | ANG | FGB | LE | |

East Midlands Trains 43061, on hire to Virgin Trains East Coast, stands at King's Cross with the 1105 to Leeds on 7 July 2016. This loco has since been named *The Fearless Foxes. Pip Dunn*

| | | | | | | |
|---|---|---|---|---|---|---|
| 43136 | ae | EFPC | ANG | FGB | LE | |
| 43137 | ae | EFPC | ANG | FGB | LE | *Newton Abbot 150* |
| 43138 | ae | EFPC | ANG | FGB | LE | |
| 43139 | ae | EFPC | ANG | FGB | LE | *Driver Stan Martin 25 June 1950-6 November 2004* |
| 43140 | ae | EFPC | ANG | FGB | LE | *Landore Diesel Depot 1963 Celebrating 50 Years 2013 – Depo Diesel Glandŵr 1963 Dathlu 50 Miynedd 2013* |
| 43141 | ae | EFPC | ANG | FGB | LE | *Cardiff Panel Signal Box 1966-2016 Blwch Signalau Panel Caerdydd 1966-2016* |
| 43142 | ae | EFPC | ANG | FGB | LE | *Reading Panel Signal Box 1965-2010* |
| 43143 | ae | EFPC | ANG | FGB | LE | *Stroud 700* |
| 43144 | ae | EFPC | ANG | FGA | LE | |
| 43145 | ae | EFPC | ANG | FGB | LE | |
| 43146 | ae | EFPC | ANG | FGA | LE | |
| 43147 | ae | EFPC | ANG | FGB | LE | *Royal Marines Celebrating 350 Years* |
| 43148 | ae | HAPC | ANG | FGU | EC | |
| 43149 | ae | EFPC | ANG | FGB | LE | *University of Plymouth* |
| 43150 | ae | EFPC | ANG | FGB | LE | |
| 43151 | ae | EFPC | ANG | FGB | LE | |
| 43152 | ae | EFPC | ANG | FGB | LE | |

| | | | | | | |
|---|---|---|---|---|---|---|
| 43153 | ae | EFPC | FIR | FGB | OO | |
| 43154 | ae | EFPC | FIR | FGB | OO | |
| 43155 | ae | EFPC | FIR | FGB | OO | *The Red Arrows 50 Seasons of Excellence* |
| 43156 | ae | EFPC | POR | FGB | OO | *Dartington International Summer School* |
| 43158 | ae | EFPC | FIR | FGB | OO | |
| 43159 | ae | EFPC | POR | FGB | OO | |
| 43160 | ae | EFPC | POR | FGB | OO | *Sir Moir Lockhead OBE* |
| 43161 | ae | EFPC | POR | FGB | OO | |
| 43162 | ae | EFPC | POR | FGB | OO | |
| 43163 | ae | EFPC | ANG | FGA | OO | |
| 43164 | ae | EFPC | ANG | FGB | OO | |
| 43165 | ae | EFPC | ANG | FGB | OO | *Prince Michael of Kent* |
| 43168 | ae | EFPC | ANG | FGB | OO | |
| 43169 | ae | EFPC | ANG | FGB | OO | *THE NATIONAL TRUST* |
| 43170 | ae | EFPC | ANG | FGB | OO | |
| 43171 | ae | EFPC | ANG | FGB | OO | |
| 43172 | ae | EFPC | ANG | HAR | OO | *Harry Patch The last survivor of the trenches* |
| 43174 | ae | EFPC | ANG | FGB | OO | |
| 43175 | ae | EFPC | ANG | FGB | OO | *GWR 175TH ANNIVERSARY* |
| 43176 | ae | EFPC | ANG | FGB | OO | |
| 43177 | ae | EFPC | ANG | FGB | OO | |
| 43179 | ae | EFPC | ANG | FGB | OO | *Pride of Laira* |
| 43180 | ae | EFPC | POR | FGB | OO | |
| 43181 | ae | EFPC | ANG | FGB | OO | |
| 43182 | ae | EFPC | ANG | FGB | OO | |
| 43183 | ae | EFPC | ANG | FGB | OO | |
| 43185 | ae | EFPC | ANG | ICS | OO | *Great Western* |
| 43186 | ae | EFPC | ANG | FGS | OO | |
| 43187 | ae | EFPC | ANG | GWT | OO | |
| 43188 | ae | EFPC | ANG | GWT | OO | |
| 43189 | ae | EFPC | ANG | FGB | OO | *RAILWAY HERITAGE TRUST* |
| 43190 | ae | EFPC | ANG | FGB | OO | |
| 43191 | ae | EFPC | ANG | FGB | OO | |
| 43192 | ae | EFPC | ANG | FGB | OO | |
| 43193 | ae | EFPC | POR | FGB | OO | |
| 43194 | ae | EFPC | FIR | GWT | OO | |
| 43195 | ae | EFPC | POR | FGB | OO | |
| 43196 | ae | EFPC | POR | FGB | OO | |
| 43197 | ae | EFPC | POR | FGB | OO | |
| 43198 | ae | EFPC | FIR | GWT | OO | |

Note: 54 EFPC locomotives are due to transfer to First ScotRail in 2017-18 in the HAPC pool. They are expected to be 43003/012/015/021/026/028/030-037, 43124-152/163/164/168/169/175-177/179/181-183.

## Class 43/2

Details as per 43/0 fitted with MTU engines

| | | | | | | | |
|---|---|---|---|---|---|---|---|
| 43206 | 43006 | ae | IECP | ANG | VEC | EC | |
| 43207 | 43007 | ae | EHPC | ANG | XCT | EC | |
| 43208 | 43008 | ae | IECP | ANG | VEC | EC | *Lincolnshire Echo* |
| 43238 | 43038 | ae | IECP | ANG | NRA | EC | *National Railway Museum 40 Years 1975-2015* |
| 43239 | 43039 | ae | IECP | ANG | VEC | EC | |
| 43251 | 43051 | ae | IECP | POR | VEC | EC | |
| 43257 | 43057 | ae | IECP | POR | VEC | EC | *Bounds Green* |

| | | | | | | | |
|---|---|---|---|---|---|---|---|
| 43272 | 43072 | ae | IECP | POR | VEC | EC | |
| 43274 | 43074 | ae | IECP | POR | VEC | EC | *Spirit of Sunderland* |
| 43277 | 43077 | ae | IECP | POR | VEC | EC | |
| 43285 | 43085 | ae | EHPC | POR | XCT | EC | |
| 43290 | 43090 | ae | IECP | POR | VEC | EC | *mtu Fascination of Power* |
| 43295 | 43095 | ae | IECP | ANG | VEC | EC | |
| 43296 | 43096 | ae | IECP | ANG | VEC | EC | |
| 43299 | 43099 | ae | IECP | POR | VEC | EC | |
| 43300 | 43100 | ae | IECP | POR | VEC | EC | *Craigentinny* |
| 43301 | 43101 | ae | EHPC | POR | XCT | EC | |
| 43302 | 43102 | ae | IECP | POR | VEC | EC | |
| 43303 | 43103 | ae | EHPC | POR | XCT | EC | |
| 43304 | 43104 | ae | EHPC | ANG | XCT | EC | |
| 43305 | 43105 | ae | IECP | ANG | VEC | EC | |
| 43306 | 43106 | ae | IECP | ANG | VEC | EC | |
| 43307 | 43107 | ae | IECP | ANG | VEC | EC | |
| 43308 | 43108 | ae | IECP | ANG | VEC | EC | *HIGHLAND CHIEFTAIN* |
| 43309 | 43109 | ae | IECP | ANG | VEC | EC | |
| 43310 | 43110 | ae | IECP | ANG | VEC | EC | |
| 43311 | 43111 | ae | IECP | ANG | VEC | EC | |
| 43312 | 43112 | ae | IECP | ANG | VEC | EC | |
| 43313 | 43113 | ae | IECP | ANG | VEC | EC | |
| 43314 | 43114 | ae | IECP | ANG | VEC | EC | |
| 43315 | 43115 | ae | IECP | ANG | VEC | EC | |
| 43316 | 43116 | ae | IECP | ANG | VEC | EC | |
| 43317 | 43117 | ae | IECP | ANG | VEC | EC | |
| 43318 | 43118 | ae | IECP | ANG | VEC | EC | |
| 43319 | 43119 | ae | IECP | ANG | VEC | EC | |
| 43320 | 43120 | ae | IECP | ANG | VEC | EC | |
| 43321 | 43121 | ae | EHPC | POR | XCT | EC | |
| 43357 | 43157 | ae | EHPC | POR | XCT | EC | |
| 43366 | 43166 | ae | EHPC | ANG | XCT | EC | |
| 43367 | 43167 | ae | IECP | ANG | VEC | EC | *DELTIC 50 1955-2005* |
| 43378 | 43178 | ae | EHPC | ANG | XCT | EC | |
| 43384 | 43184 | ae | EHPC | ANG | XCT | EC | |
| 43423 | 43123 | aej | GCHP | ANG | GCR | HT | *VALENTA 1972-2010* |
| 43465 | 43065 | aej | GCHP | ANG | GCR | HT | |
| 43467 | 43068 | aej | GCHP | ANG | GCR | HT | |
| 43468 | 43068 | aej | GCHP | ANG | GCR | HT | |
| 43480 | 43080 | aej | GCHP | ANG | GCR | HT | |
| 43484 | 43084 | aej | GCHP | ANG | GCR | HT | *PETER FOX 1942-2011 PLATFORM 5* |

43274 has 'Spirit of Sunderland' branding
43295 has 'Perth is the Place' branding
43300 has 'Craigentinny 100 1914-2014' branding

## Class 47

*BR's standard Type 4 diesel electric, 512 were built between 1962-68. Mass withdrawals started in 1986, but a few have found use with some private operators. 33 were rebuilt as Class 57s.*

| | |
|---|---|
| Built by: | Brush, Loughborough and BR Crewe |
| Years introduced: | 1962-68 |
| Wheel arrangement: | Co-Co |
| Weight: | 111-121 tons |
| Length: | 63ft 6in (19.38m) |
| Engine Type: | Sulzer 12LDA28C |

| | |
|---|---|
| Engine output: | 2,580hp (1,922kW) |
| Power at rail: | 2,080hp (1,550kW) |
| Tractive effort: | 60,000lbf (267kN) |
| Continuous tractive effort: | 30,000lbf (133kN) |
| Maximum design speed: | 95mph (152km/h) |
| Brake Force: | 60 tons |
| Route Availability: | 6 |
| Main generator type: | Brush TG160-60 Mk 2, TG160-60 Mk 4 or TM172-50 Mk 1 |
| Auxiliary generator type: | Brush TG69-20 or TG69-28 Mk 2 |
| Traction Motor type: | Brush TM64-68 or TM64-68 Mk 1 |
| Fuel tank capacity: | 727 (3,273lit), t – 1,308gal (5,887lit) |
| Multiple Working type: (where fitted) | Green Circle |

## Class 47/0s – standard locos

| | | | | | | | |
|---|---|---|---|---|---|---|---|
| 47194 | D1844 | aotm | AWCX | WCR | RFD | CS (U) | |
| 47236 | D1913 | aotm | | WCR | RFE | CS (U) | |
| 47237 | D1914 | xotm | AWCA | WCR | WCR | CS | |
| 47245 | D1922 | xotmp* | AWCA | WCR | WCR | CS | |
| 47270 | D1971 | ao | AWCA | WCR | BRB | CS | *SWIFT* |

## Class 47/3 – built with no train heating

Details as per Class 47/0 except:

Multiple Working type (where fitted): Green Circle

| | | | | | | | |
|---|---|---|---|---|---|---|---|
| 47355 | D1836 | aotm | AWCX | WCR | FRG | CS (U) | |
| 47368 | D1887 | xo | | WCR | TTG | CS (U) | |

## Class 47/4 – ETH fitted

Details as per Class 47/0 except:

ETH alternator type: Brush BL100-30

ETH index: 66

Fuel tank capacity: 727 (3,273lit), t – 1,230gal (5,537lit)

Multiple Working type (where fitted): DRS system

| | | | | | | | |
|---|---|---|---|---|---|---|---|
| 47492 | D1760 | xe | AWCX | WCR | RES | CS (U) | |
| 47500 | D1943, 47770 | xet | AWCX | WCR | WCR | CS (U) | |
| 47501 | D1944 | aetm | MBDL | LSL | GYP | CD | *CRAFTSMAN* |
| 47526 | D1109 | xe | | WCR | LLB | CS (U) | |
| 47580 | D1762, 47167, 47732 | xet | MBDL | SFG | BRF | CS | *County of Essex*Note 47580 is RA7 |

## Class 47/7 – Converted locos for Rail Express Systems

Details as per Class 47/4

Multiple Working type (where fitted): Green Circle or DRS system (47790)

| | | | | | | | |
|---|---|---|---|---|---|---|---|
| 47727 | D1629, 47047, 47569 | aetm | COLS | COL | COL | WH | *Rebecca* |
| 47739 | D1615, 47035, 47594 | aetm | COLS | COL | COL | WH | *Robin of Templecombe 1938-2013* |
| 47746 | D1754, 47160, 47605 | xet | AWCA | WCR | WCR | CS | *Chris Fudge 29.7.70-22.6.10* |

| | | | | | | | |
|---|---|---|---|---|---|---|---|
| 47749 | D1660, 47076, 47625 | aetm | COLS | COL | COL | WH | *CITY OF TRURO* |
| 47760 | D1617, 47036, 47562, 47672 | xetp* | AWCA | WCR | WCR | CS | |
| 47768 | D1725, 47490 | xet | AWCX | WCR | UND | CS (U) | |
| 47772 | D1657, 47537 | xet | AWCA | WCR | WCR | CS | |
| 47773 | D1755, 47541 | xetp | MBDL | VIN | GYP | TM | |
| 47776 | D1776, 47181, 47578 | xetp | AWCX | WCR | RES | CS (U) | |
| 47786 | D1730, 47138, 47607, 47821 | aet | AWCA | WCR | WCR | CS (U) | *Roy Castle OBE* |
| 47787 | D1757, 47163, 47610, 47823 | aet | AWCX | WCR | WCR | CS (U) | *Windsor Castle* |
| 47790 | D1973, 47272, 47593, 47673 | aetmp | MBDL | LSL | NBU | CD (U) | |
| 47798 | D1656, 47072, 47609, 47834 | xet | MBDL | NRM | RTP | YK | *Prince William* |

## Class 47/4 continued

Multiple Working type: (where fitted) Green Circle (47812/815/843/847/848) or DRS system (47802/805/813/832/841)

| | | | | | | | |
|---|---|---|---|---|---|---|---|
| 47802 | D1950, 47552 | xetm | AWCA | WCR | WCR | CS | |
| 47804 | D1965, 47265, 47591, 47792 | xet | AWCA | WCR | WCR | CS | |
| 47805 | D1935, 47257, 47650 | aetm | MBDL | LSL | GYP | CD (U) | |
| 47811 | D1719, 47128, 47656 | aet | | LSL | FPG | CD (U) | |
| 47812 | D1916, 47239, 47657 | aetm | SROG | ROG | OXB | BU | |
| 47813 | D1720, 47129, 47658 | aetm | SROG | ROG | ROG | LR | |
| 47815 | D1748, 47155, 47660 | aetm | SROG | ROG | OXB | LR (U) | |
| 47816 | D1650, 47066, 47661 | aet | | LSL | FPG | CD (U) | |
| 47826 | D1976, 47274, 47637 | aet | AWCA | WCR | WCR | CS | |
| 47830 | D1645, 47061, 47649 | aet | DFLH | FLI | GYP | CB | *BEECHING'S LEGACY* |
| 47832 | D1610, 47031, 47560 | aetm | AWCA | WCR | WCR | CS | |
| 47841 | D1726, 47134, 47622 | aetm | MBDL | LSL | DRU | CD (U) | |
| 47843 | D1676, 47090, 47623 | aetm | SROG | ROG | OXB | LR (U) | |
| 47847 | D1774, 47179, 47577 | aetm | SROG | ROG | LLB | LR (U) | |
| 47848 | D1652, 47068, 47632 | aetm | GROG | ROG | OXB | BU | |
| 47851 | D1648, 47064, 47639 | aet | AWCA | WCR | WCR | CS | |
| 47854 | D1972, 47271, 47604, 47674 | aetp* | AWCA | WCR | WCR | CS | *Diamond Jubilee* |

47580 *County of Essex* is owned by the Stratford Class 47 Group but has full main line registration and spends the vast majority of its time on hire to West Coast Railways. On 26 May 2013 it passes Giggleswick with 5Z64, the 1223 Derby-Carnforth ECS move. *Anthony Hicks*

## Class 50

*A fleet of 50 Type 4 diesel electrics built in 1967/68 and withdrawn by 1994. The main line survivors are essentially preserved but do find spot hire use.*

| | |
|---|---|
| Built by: | English Electric Vulcan Foundry |
| Years introduced: | 1967-68 |
| Wheel arrangement: | Co-Co |
| Weight: | 117 tons |
| Length: | 68ft 6in (20.87m) |
| Engine Type: | English Electric 16CSVT |
| Engine output: | 2,700hp (2,014kW) |
| Power at rail: | 2,070hp (1,540kW) |
| Tractive effort: | 48,500lbf (216kN) |
| Continuous tractive effort: | 33,000lbf (147kN) |
| ETH generator type: | EE915-1B |
| ETH index: | 61 |
| Maximum design speed: | 100mph (160km/h) |
| Brake Force: | 59 tons |
| Route Availability: | 6 |
| Main generator type: | EE840-4B |
| Auxiliary generator type: | EE911-5C |
| Traction Motor type: | EE538-5A |
| Fuel tank capacity: | 1,055gal (4,797lit) |
| Multiple Working type: | Orange Square |

50007 *Hercules* is one of six main line registered, but essentially preserved, Class 50s. Now owned by the Class 50 Alliance, back on 17 May 2014 the loco was owned by Neil Boden and often hired by Colas Rail Freight. Leading 56105, the BR blue 50 works 6E07, the 0859 Washwood Heath-Boston Docks, past Lea Marston near Water Orton. *Anthony Hicks*

| | | | | | | | |
|---|---|---|---|---|---|---|---|
| 50007 | D407 | xep | CFOL | CFA | BRB | KR | *Hercules* |
| 50008 | D408 | xep | HTLX | GAR | LAB | WH | *Thunderer* |
| 50017 | D417 | xep | BREL | BOD | NSO | WH | *Royal Oak* |
| 50044 | D444 | xep | CFOL | CFA | BRB | KR (U) | *Exeter* |
| 50049 | D449, 50149 | xep* | CFOL | CFA | BRL | KR | *Defiance* |
| 50050 | D400 | xep | BREL | BOD | BRB | WH | *Fearless* |

## Class 52

*Type 4 diesel hydraulic design, with 74 locos built but all withdrawn by 1977. The sole main line survivor, one of seven which are preserved, is used mostly on occasional charter trains and is not in day to day use.*

| | |
|---|---|
| Built by: | BR Swindon or Crewe |
| Years introduced: | 1961-64 |
| Wheel arrangement: | C-C |
| Weight: | 108 tons |
| Length: | 68ft (20.73m) |
| Engine Type: | two Maybach MD655 |
| Total Engine output: | 2,700hp (2,014kW) |
| Power at rail: | 2,350hp (1,753kW) |
| Tractive effort: | 66,700lbf (297kN) |
| Continuous tractive effort: | 45,200lbf (201kN) |
| Maximum design speed: | 90mph (144km/h) |

| | |
|---|---|
| Brake Force: | 82 tons |
| Route Availability: | 6 |
| Transmission type: | Voith L630rU |
| Fuel tank capacity: | 850gal (3,825lit) |
| Multiple Working type: | None |

| | | | | | | |
|---|---|---|---|---|---|---|
| D1015 | XO | MBDL | DTG | MFY | KR | *WESTERN CHAMPION* |

## Class 55

*An English Electric twin-engine Type 5 passenger design, just 22 were built for ECML work. All were withdrawn by 1982. Six survivors are preserved but see occasional spot hire use. Just 55009 is currently working on both engines.*

| | |
|---|---|
| Built by: | English Electric, Vulcan Foundry |
| Years introduced: | 1961-62 |
| Wheel arrangement: | Co-Co |
| Weight: | 100 tons |
| Length: | 69ft 6in (21.18m) |
| Engine Type: | two Napier D18-25 'Deltic' |
| Engine output: | 3,300hp (2,460kW) |
| Power at rail: | 2,460hp (1,969kW) |
| Tractive effort: | 50,000lbf (222kN) |
| Continuous tractive effort: | 30,500lbf (136kN) |
| ETH index: | 66 |
| Maximum design speed: | 100mph (160km/h) |
| Brake Force: | 51 tons |
| Route Availability: | 5 |
| Main generator type: | two English Electric EE829-1A |
| Auxiliary generator type: | two English Electric EE913-1A |
| Traction Motor type: | English Electric EE538A |
| Fuel tank capacity: | 826gal (3,717lit), 1,626gal (7,317lit) – 55022 |
| Multiple Working type: | None |

One of three Class 55s registered for main line running is 55009 *Alycidon*, On 9 April 2016 it works a Derby-Tweedbank charter past Galabank on the newly re-opened line in the Scottish Borders. *Anthony Hicks*

| | | | | | | | |
|---|---|---|---|---|---|---|---|
| 55002 | D9002 | xe | DBLX | NRM | GYP | YK | *THE KING'S OWN YORKSHIRE LIGHT INFANTRY* |
| 55009 | D9009 | xe | DBLX | DPS | BRB | BH | *ALYCIDON* |
| 55022 | D9000 | xet | ELRD | BEV | BRB | NY (U) | *ROYAL SCOTS GREY** |

* loco currently running as 55018 *BALLYMOSS*

## Class 56

*Type 5 freight loco built from 1976 to 1984. First 30 locos were built in Romania, remainder built at Doncaster and Crewe. Withdrawn by EWS in March 2004, a few have found use with spot hire companies, DC Rail and Colas Rail Freight.*

| | |
|---|---|
| Built by: | Electroputere in Craiovia Romania, BREL Doncaster and Crewe. |
| Years introduced: | 1976-84 |
| Wheel arrangement: | Co-Co |
| Weight: | 126 tons |
| Length: | 63ft 6in (19.39m) |
| Engine Type: | Ruston Paxman 16RK3CT |
| Engine output: | 3,250hp (2,420kW) |
| Power at rail: | 2,400hp (1,790kW) |
| Tractive effort: | 61,800lbf (275kN) |
| Continuous tractive effort: | 53,950lbf (240kN) |
| Maximum design speed: | 80mph (128km/h) |
| Brake Force: | 60 tons |
| Route Availability: | 7 |
| Main alternator type: | Brush BA1101A |
| Auxiliary alternator type: | Brush BAA602A |
| Traction Motor type: | Brush TMH73-62 |
| Fuel tank capacity: | 1,150gal (5,228lit) |
| Multiple Working type: | Red Diamond |

| | | | | | | | |
|---|---|---|---|---|---|---|---|
| 56049 | | aos | COLS | COL | COL | WH (U) | |
| 56051 | | aos | COLS | COL | FER | LR (U) | |
| 56078 | | aos | COFS | COL | COL | WH | |
| 56081 | | aos | UKRL | UKR | UKG | LR | |
| 56087 | | aos | COFS | COL | COL | WH | |
| 56090 | | aos | COLS | COL | COL | WH (U) | |
| 56091 | | aos | HTLX | DCR | FEU | WH | |
| 56094 | | aosr | COLS | COL | COL | WH (S) | |
| 56096 | | aos | COLS | COL | COL | WH (S) | |
| 56098 | | aos | UKRL | UKR | RFO | LR | *Lost Boys 68-88* |
| 56103 | | aos | HTLX | DCR | FEU | WH | |
| 56104 | | aos | UKRL | UKR | UKG | LR | |
| 56105 | | aos | COFS | COL | COL | WH | |
| 56113 | | aos | COFS | COL | COL | WH | |
| 56128 | | aos | HTLX | DCR | TRN | WH (U) | |
| 56301 | 56045 | aos | UKRL | CFS | JFU | LR | |
| 56302 | 56124 | aosr | COFS | COL | COL | WH | *PECO The Railway Modeller 2016 70 years* |
| 56303 | 56125 | aos | HTLX | DCR | DCG | WH | |
| 56311 | 56057 | aos | HTLS | DCR | DCR | WH | |
| 56312 | 56003 | aos | HTLS | DCR | DCR | WH | *Jeremiah Dixon Son of County Durham Surveyor of the Mason – Dixon Line U.S.A.* |

## Class 57

*Brush built locos using the bodies and bogies from redundant Class 47s and re-engineered with second hand GM engines. Initial order was with Freightliner, for up to 30 locos, but cut back to 12. 57601 was a demonstrator ETH version, later sold to WCR while Virgin Trains ordered 16 and First Great Western four. Six 57/3 were briefly with Network Rail and three 57/0s were briefly with Advenza. The fleet is now split between DRS, GWR and WCR.*

| | |
|---|---|
| Rebuilt by: | Brush Traction |
| Years introduced: | 1998-99 |
| Wheel arrangement: | Co-Co |
| Weight: | 121 tons |
| Length: | 63ft 6in (19.38m) |
| Engine Type: | General Motors 645-12E3 |
| Engine output: | 2,500hp (1,860kW) |
| Power at rail: | 2,025hp (1,507kW) |
| Tractive effort: | 55,000lbf (245kN) |
| Continuous tractive effort | 31,500lbf (140kN) |
| Maximum design speed: | 75mph (121km/h) |
| Brake Force: | 80 tons |
| Route Availability: | 6 |
| Main alternator type: | Brush BA1101A |
| Auxiliary alternator type: | Brush BAA602A |
| Traction Motor type: | Brush TM68-46 |
| Fuel tank capacity: | 1,221gal (5,550lit) |
| Multiple Working type: | Green Circle (where fitted) |

## Class 57/0 – original locos built for Freightliner without train heating

| | | | | | | | |
|---|---|---|---|---|---|---|---|
| 57001 | D1875, 47356 | ao | AWCA | WCR | WCR | CS (U) | |
| 57002 | D1803, 47322 | aom | XHCK | DRS | DRN | KM | *RAIL Express* |
| 57003 | D1798, 47317 | aom | XHSS | DRS | DRN | KM | |
| 57004 | D1828, 47347 | aom | XHSS | DRS | DRC | LT (S) | |
| 57005 | D1831, 47350 | ao | AWCX | WCR | ADZ | CS (U) | |
| 57006 | D1837, 47187 | ao | AWCX | WCR | WCR | CS (U) | |
| 57007 | D1813, 47332 | aom | XHCK | DRS | DRN | KM | |
| 57008 | D1644, 47060 | aom | XHSS | DRS | DRC | LT (S) | |
| 57009 | D1664, 47079 | aom | XHSS | DRS | DRC | LT (S) | |
| 57010 | D1907, 47231 | aom | XHSS | DRS | DRN | LT (U) | |
| 57011 | D1810, 47329 | aom | XHSS | DRS | DRC | ZG (U) | |
| 57012 | D1854, 47204 | aom | XHSS | DRS | DRC | LT (S) | |

## Class 57/3 – ETH locos originally ordered by Virgin Trains

| | |
|---|---|
| Years introduced: | 2002-04 |
| Engine Type: | General Motors 645-12F3B |
| Engine output: | 2,750hp (2,051kW) |
| Power at rail: | 2,200hp (1,640kW) |
| Weight: | 117 tons |
| Main alternator type: | Brush BA1101F or BA1101G |
| ETH alternator type: | Brush BAA |
| ETH index: | 100 |
| Maximum design speed: | 95mph (153km/h) |
| Brake Force: | 60 tons |

Fuel tank capacity: 1,308gal (5,887lit)
Multiple Working type: None

| | | | | | | | |
|---|---|---|---|---|---|---|---|
| 57301 | D1653, 47069, 47638, 47845 | aedr | XHAC | POR | DRN | KM | *Goliath* |
| 57302 | D1928, 47251, 47589, 47827 | aed | XHSS | DRS | DRC | LT (U) | *Chad Varah* |
| 57303 | D1957, 47554, 47705 | aed | XHAC | POR | DRN | KM | *Pride of Carlisle* |
| 57304 | D1639, 47055, 47652, 47807 | aed | XHVT | DRS | DRN | KM | *Pride of Cheshire* |
| 57305 | D1758, 47164, 47571, 47822 | aed | XHAC | POR | NOB | KM | *Northern Princess* |
| 57306 | D1919, 47242, 47659, 47814 | aed | XHAC | POR | DRN | KM | *Her Majesty's Railway Inspectorate 175* |
| 57307 | D1901, 47225 | aed | XHVT | DRS | DRN | KM | *LADY PENELOPE* |
| 57308 | D1677, 47091, 47647, 47846 | aed | XHVT | DRS | DRN | KM | *James Ferguson* |
| 57309 | D1931, 47254, 47651, 47806 | aed | XHVT | DRS | DRN | KM | *Pride of Crewe* |
| 57310 | D1618, 47037, 47563, 47831 | aedr | XHAC | POR | DRN | KM | *Pride of Cumbria* |
| 57311 | D1611, 47032, 47662, 47817 | aed | XHVT | DRS | DRC | KM | *Thunderbird* |
| 57312 | D1811, 47330 | aedr | XHAC | POR | NOB | KM | *Solway Princess* |
| 57313 | D1890, 47371 | ae | AWCA | WCR | WCR | CS | |
| 57314 | D1891, 47372 | ae | AWCA | WCR | WCR | CS | |
| 57315 | D1911, 47234 | ae | AWCA | WCR | WCR | CS | |
| 57316 | D1992, 47290 | ae | AWCA | WCR | WCR | CS | |

57307 has '20 years of Direct Rail Services' branding

Class 57s, rebuilt and re-engined Class 47s, are in use with DRS, WCR and GWR. On 16 March 2014, WCR's 57315 works 5Z26, the 1122 Hull-Carnforth ECS, past Burton Salmon, near Castleford. *Anthony Hicks*

## Class 57/6 – locos fitted with ETH

Details as per Class 57/3 except:

| | |
|---|---|
| Years introduced: | 2001 |
| Weight: | 113 tons |
| Main alternator type: | Brush BA1101E |
| ETH index: | 95 |
| Fuel tank capacity: | 727gal (3,273lit) |

| | | | | | | | |
|---|---|---|---|---|---|---|---|
| 57601 | D1759, 47165, 47590, 47825 | ae | AWCA | WCR | WCR | CS | |
| 57602 | D1818, 47337 | aep* | EFOO | POR | GWT | OO | *Restormel Castle* |
| 57603 | D1830, 47349 | aep* | EFOO | POR | GWT | OO | *Tintagel Castle* |
| 57604 | D1859, 47209 | aep* | EFOO | POR | GWR | OO | *PENDENNIS CASTLE* |
| 57605 | D1856, 47206 | aep* | EFOO | POR | GWT | OO | *Totnes Castle* |

## Class 59

*The four Class 59/0s, owned by Foster Yeoman, were the first privately-owned main line diesels to run on BR, in 1986. FY later ordered a fifth loco while ARC ordered four 59/1s which were delivered in 1990 and National Power ordered six Class 59/2s. The latter are now owned by DB Cargo. 59003 spent 1997-2014 in Germany until purchased by GB Railfreight.*

| | |
|---|---|
| Built by: | GM-EMD, La Grange, Illinois, USA |
| Years introduced: | 1985-95 |
| Wheel arrangement: | Co-Co |
| Weight: | 121 tons |
| Length: | 70ft (21.40m) |
| Engine Type: | EMD 16-645E3C |
| Engine output: | 3,000hp (2,238kW) |
| Power at rail: | 2,533hp (1,889kW) |
| Tractive effort: | 113,550lbf (506kN) |
| Continuous tractive effort | 65,300lbf (291kN) |
| Maximum design speed: | 60mph (96km/h) |
| Brake Force: | 69 tons |
| Route Availability: | 7 |
| Traction alternator: | EMD AR11 |
| Companion alternator: | EMD D14A |
| Auxiliary alternator: | EMD 3A8147 |
| Traction Motor type: | EMD D77B |
| Fuel tank capacity: | 1,000gal (4,546lit) |
| Multiple Working type: | AAR |

## Class 59/0 – original Foster Yeoman locos

| | | | | | | |
|---|---|---|---|---|---|---|
| 59001 | aos | XYPO | AGI | AGI | MD | *YEOMAN ENDEAVOUR* |
| 59002 | aos | XYPO | AGI | AGI | MD | *ALAN J DAY* |
| 59003 | aos | GBYH | GBR | GBR | RR | *YEOMAN HIGHLANDER* |
| 59004 | aos | XYPO | AGI | AGI | MD | *PAUL A HAMMOND* |
| 59005 | aos | XYPO | AGI | AGI | MD | *KENNETH J PAINTER* |

## Class 59/1 – original ARC locos

| | | | | | | |
|---|---|---|---|---|---|---|
| 59101 | aos | XYPA | HAN | HAN | MD | *Village of Whatley* |
| 59102 | aos | XYPA | HAN | HAN | MD | *Village of Chantry* |
| 59103 | aos | XYPA | HAN | HAN | MD | *Village of Mells* |
| 59104 | aos | XYPA | HAN | HAN | MD | *Village of Great Elm* |

## Class 59/2 – original National Power locos

| | | | | | | |
|---|---|---|---|---|---|---|
| 59201 | aos | WDAM | DBC | DBC | MD | |
| 59202 | aos | WDAM | DBC | DBC | MD | *Alan Meddows Taylor MD Mendip Rail Limited* |
| 59203 | aos | WDAM | DBC | DBC | MD | |
| 59204 | aos | WDAM | DBC | DBC | MD | |
| 59205 | aos | WDAM | DBC | DBC | MD | |
| 59206 | aos | WDAM | DBC | DBC | MD | *John F Yeoman Rail Pioneer* |

## Class 60

*Heavy freight Type 5 built by Brush, the last diesel locos delivered to BR. All inherited by EWS (Now DB Cargo). The fleet has been steadily run down since 2004 with ten locos sold to Colas Rail Freight and 20 more likely to move to Wabtec for overhaul and reuse, possibly with GBRf. DBC retains a fluctuating fleet of about 20 overhauled locos.*

| | |
|---|---|
| Built by: | Brush Traction, Loughborough |
| Years introduced: | 1989-1993 |
| Wheel arrangement: | Co-Co |
| Weight: | 129-130 tons |
| Length: | 70ft (21.34m) |
| Engine Type: | Mirrlees MB275T |
| Engine output: | 3,100hp (2,240kW) |
| Power at rail: | 2,415hp (1,800kW) |
| Tractive effort: | 106,500lbf (500kN) |
| Continuous tractive effort | 71,570lbf (336kN) |
| Maximum design speed: | 62mph (99km/h) |
| Brake Force: | 74 tons |
| Route Availability: | 7 |
| Main alternator type: | Brush BA1000 |
| Auxiliary alternator type: | Brush BAA700 |
| Traction Motor type: | Brush TM216 |
| Fuel tank capacity: | 990gal (4,500lit) |
| Multiple Working type: | Within Class only |

| | | | | | | |
|---|---|---|---|---|---|---|
| 60001 | aos | WCAT | DBC | DBC | TO | |
| 60002 | aost | COLO | COL | COL | RU | |
| 60003 | aost | WQDA | WAB | EWS | TO (U) | *FREIGHT TRANSPORT ASSOCIATION* |
| 60004 | aost | WQDA | WAB | EWS | TY (U) | |
| 60005 | aost | WQDA | WAB | EWS | TY (U) | |
| 60006 | aos | WQDA | WAB | COR | TY (U) | |
| 60007 | aost | WCBT | DBC | DBC | TO | *The Spirit of Tom Kendall* |
| 60008 | aos | WQDA | WAB | EWS | TC (U) | *Sir William McAlpine* |
| 60009 | aost | WQBA | DBC | EWS | TC (U) | |
| 60010 | aost | WQAB | DBC | DBC | TO (U) | |
| 60011 | aos | WCAT | DBC | DBC | TO | |
| 60012 | aost | WQBA | DBC | EWS | TC (U) | |
| 60013 | aos | WQDA | WAB | TEW | TO (U) | *Robert Boyle* |
| 60014 | aos | WQDA | WAB | TEW | TY (U) | |
| 60015 | aost | WCBT | DBC | DBC | TO | |
| 60017 | aost | WCBT | DBC | DBC | TO | |
| 60018 | aos | WQDA | WAB | EWS | TY (U) | |
| 60019 | aos | WCAT | DBC | DBC | TO | *Port of Grimsby & Immingham* |

| | | | | | | |
|---|---|---|---|---|---|---|
| 60020 | aost | WCBT | DBC | DBC | TO | *The Willows* |
| 60021 | aost | COLO | COL | COL | RU | |
| 60022 | aost | WQDA | WAB | EWS | TO (U) | |
| 60023 | aost | WQDA | WAB | EWS | TY (U) | |
| 60024 | aos | WQAB | DBC | DBC | TO (U) | *Clitheroe Castle* |
| 60025 | aost | WQDA | WAB | EWS | TY (U) | |
| 60026 | aost | COLO | COL | COL | RU | |
| 60027 | aost | WQDA | WAB | EWS | TY (U) | |
| 60028 | aost | WQCA | DBC | TEW | CE (U) | |
| 60029 | aos | WQCA | DBC | EWS | CE (U) | |
| 60030 | aost | WQDA | WAB | EWS | TO (U) | |
| 60031 | aos | WQDA | WAB | EWS | TY (U) | |
| 60032 | aos | WQDA | WAB | TRN | TY (U) | |
| 60033 | aost | WQCA | DBC | COR | TC (U) | *Tees Steel Express* |
| 60034 | aos | WQBA | DBC | TEW | TO (U) | |
| 60035 | aos | WQAB | DBC | EWS | TO (U) | |
| 60036 | aos | WQBA | DBC | EWS | TC (U) | *GEFCO* |
| 60037 | aost | WQDA | DBC | EWS | TY (U) | |
| 60038 | aost | WQCA | DBC | EWS | CE (U) | |
| 60039 | aos | WCAT | DBC | DBC | TO | *Dove Holes* |
| 60040 | aos | WQAA | DBC | DBC | MG (U) | *The Territorial Army Centenary* |
| 60041 | aost | WQCA | DBC | EWS | TC (U) | |
| 60042 | aos | WQDA | WAB | EWS | TY (U) | |
| 60043 | aos | WQBA | DBC | EWS | TO (U) | |
| 60044 | aos | WCAT | DBC | DBC | TO | *Dowlow* |
| 60045 | aos | WQAB | DBC | EWS | TC (U) | *The Permanent Way Institution* |
| 60046 | aost | WQCA | DBC | TEW | CE (U) | |
| 60047 | aos | COLO | COL | COL | RU | |
| 60048 | aos | WQCA | DBC | EWS | TO (U) | |
| 60049 | aos | WQAB | DBC | EWS | TO (U) | |
| 60050 | aos | WQDA | WAB | EWS | TY (U) | |
| 60051 | aost | WQDA | WAB | EWS | TO (U) | |
| 60052 | aost | WQDA | WAB | EWS | TO (U) | *Glofa Tŵr The last deep mine in Wales Tower Colliery* |
| 60053 | aos | WQBA | WAB | EWS | TY (U) | |
| 60054 | aost | WCBT | DBC | DBC | TO | |
| 60055 | aost | WQCA | DBC | TEW | CE (U) | |
| 60056 | aost | COLO | COL | COL | RU | |
| 60057 | aos | WQBA | DBC | TEW | TO (U) | *Adam Smith* |
| 60058 | aost | WQBA | DBC | EWS | TO (U) | |
| 60059 | aost | WCBT | DBC | DBC | TO | *Swinden Dalesman* |
| 60060 | aos | WQBA | DBC | TEW | TY (U) | |
| 60061 | aos | WQCA | DBC | TRN | TC (U) | |
| 60062 | aos | WQAB | DBC | DBC | TO (U) | *Stainless Pioneer* |
| 60063 | aos | WCAT | DBC | DBC | TO | |
| 60064 | aost | WQBA | DBC | TEW | TO (U) | *Back Tor* |
| 60065 | aos | WCAT | DBC | EWS | TO | *SPIRIT OF JAGUAR* |
| 60066 | aos | WCAT | DBC | DRA | TO | |
| 60067 | aos | WQBA | DBC | TEW | TY (U) | |
| 60068 | aos | WQBA | DBC | TEW | TO (U) | |
| 60069 | aos | WQBA | DBC | EWS | TC (U) | *Slioch* |
| 60070 | aost | WQBA | DBC | TLH | TO (U) | |
| 60071 | aost | WQAB | DBC | EWS | TO (U) | *Ribblehead Viaduct* |
| 60072 | aos | WQBA | DBC | TEW | TC (U) | |

One of the ten Class 60s owned and operated by Colas Rail Freight, 60076 heads an Inverness-Oxwellmains cement train past Slochd on the Highland Main Line on 2 September 2017. *Anthony Hicks*

| | | | | | | | |
|---|---|---|---|---|---|---|---|
| 60073 | | aos | WQBA | DBC | TEW | TO (U) | *Cairn Gorm* |
| 60074 | | aos | WCAT | DBC | DBC | TO | |
| 60075 | | aos | WQBA | DBC | EWS | TC (U) | |
| 60076 | | aos | COLO | COL | COL | RU | *Dunbar* |
| 60077 | | aost | WQBA | DBC | TEW | TC (U) | |
| 60078 | | aos | WQBA | DBC | MEW | TY (U) | |
| 60079 | | aos | WQAB | DBC | DBC | TO (U) | |
| 60080 | | aost | WQBA | DBC | EWS | TO (U) | |
| 60081 | | aost | WQBA | DBC | GWR | TY (U) | |
| 60082 | | aos | WQBA | DBC | TEW | CE (U) | |
| 60083 | | aos | WQBA | DBC | EWS | TY (U) | |
| 60084 | | aos | WQBA | DBC | TEW | TC (U) | |
| 60085 | | aos | COLO | COL | COL | RU | |
| 60086 | | aos | WQBA | DBC | TEW | TY (U) | |
| 60087 | | aos | COLO | COL | COL | RU | *CLIC Sargent* |
| 60088 | | aos | WQBA | DBC | TEW | TY (U) | |
| 60089 | | aost | WQBA | DBC | EWS | TY (U) | |
| 60090 | | aost | WQBA | DBC | TEW | TC (U) | |
| 60091 | | aost | WCBT | DBC | DBC | TO | *Barry Needham* |
| 60092 | | aost | WQAA | DBC | DBC | TO (S) | |
| 60093 | | aos | WQBA | DBC | EWS | TY (U) | |
| 60094 | | aos | WQBA | DBC | EWS | TC (U) | *Rugby Flyer* |
| 60095 | | aos | COLO | COL | COL | RU | |
| 60096 | | aost | COLO | COL | COL | RU | |
| 60097 | | aost | WQBA | DBC | EWS | TY (U) | |
| 60098 | | aost | WQBA | DBC | EWS | TC (U) | |
| 60099 | | aos | WQAB | DBC | TAS | TO (U) | |
| 60100 | | aos | WCAT | DBC | DBC | TO | |
| 60500 | 60016 | aos | WQBA | DBC | EWS | TO (U) | |

60007 has 'SWITCH ON TO SAFETY' branding

## Class 66

*EWS ordered 250 locos in 1996 which were delivered in 1998-2000, and since then Freightliner, GBRf, DRS and Fastline Freight (now defunct) placed orders. DBC has moved many locos to France and Poland while Freightliner has also redeployed some locos to Poland. Some have been renumbered and three written off.*

| | |
|---|---|
| Built by: | General Motors, London, Canada or EMD Muncie Indiana USA |
| Years introduced: | 1998-2000 |
| Wheel arrangement: | Co-Co |
| Weight: | 126 tons |
| Length: | 70ft 1in (21.40m) |
| Engine Type: | GM 12N-710G3B-EC |
| Engine output: | 3,300hp (2,462kW) |
| Power at rail: | 3,000hp (2,238kW) |
| Maximum tractive effort: | 92,000lbf (409kN) |
| Continuous tractive effort: | 58,390lbf (260kN) |
| Maximum design speed: | 75mph (120km/h) |
| Brake Force: | 68 tons |
| Route Availability: | 7 |
| Traction alternator: | GM-EMD AR8 |
| Companion alternator: | GM-EMD CA6 |
| Traction Motor type: | GM-EMD D43TR |
| Fuel tank capacity: | 1,440gal (6,550lit) |
| Multiple Working type: | AAR |

## Class 66/0 – locos ordered by EWS (Now DB Cargo)

| | | | | | |
|---|---|---|---|---|---|
| 66001 | aosck | WBTT | DBC | DBC | TO |
| 66002 | aos | WBAT | DBC | EWS | TO |
| 66003 | aos | WBAT | DBC | EWS | TO |
| 66004 | aosk | WBAE | DBC | EWS | TO |
| 66005 | aos | WBAT | DBC | EWS | TO |
| 66006 | aos | WBAT | DBC | EWS | TO |
| 66007 | aoskq | WBAR | DBC | EWS | TO |
| 66008 | aosk | WQDA | GBR | EWS | TO (U) |
| 66009 | aosk | WBAE | DBC | DBC | TO |
| 66011 | aosk | WBAE | DBC | EWS | TO |
| 66012 | aosk | WBAT | DBC | EWS | TO |
| 66013 | aosk | WBAE | DBC | EWS | TO |
| 66014 | aosk | WBAR | DBC | EWS | TO |
| 66015 | aosk | WBAR | DBC | EWS | TO |
| 66016 | aosk | WQDA | GBR | DBC | TO |
| 66017 | aosckq | WBTT | DBC | DBC | TO |
| 66018 | aosk | WBAE | DBC | DBC | TO |
| 66019 | aosckq | WBTT | DBC | DBC | TO (U) |
| 66020 | aosk | WBAE | DBC | DBC | TO |
| 66021 | aoskq | WBAR | DBC | EWS | TO |
| 66023 | aos | WBAT | DBC | EWS | TO |
| 66024 | aosk | WBAE | DBC | EWS | TO |
| 66025 | aoskq | WBAR | DBC | EWS | TO |
| 66027 | aos | WBAT | DBC | EWS | TO |
| 66030 | aosq | WBAR | DBC | EWS | TO |
| 66031 | aos | WBAT | DBC | EWS | TO |
| 66034 | aosk | WBAE | DBC | DBC | TO |
| 66035 | aosk | WBAE | DBC | EWS | TO |

| | | | | | | |
|---|---|---|---|---|---|---|
| 66037 | aoskq | WBAR | DBC | EWS | TO | |
| 66039 | aosk | WBAE | DBC | EWS | TO | |
| 66040 | aoskq | WBAR | DBC | EWS | TO | |
| 66041 | aosk | WBAE | DBC | DBC | TO | |
| 66043 | aosk | WQAA | DBC | EWS | TO (U) | |
| 66044 | aosk | WBAE | DBC | DBC | TO | |
| 66046 | aosk | WQDA | GBR | EWS | TO (U) | |
| 66047 | aos | WBAT | DBC | EWS | TO | |
| 66050 | aosk | WBAE | DBC | EWS | TO | *EWS Energy* |
| 66051 | aoskq | WBAR | DBC | EWS | TO | |
| 66053 | aosk | WBAE | DBC | EWS | TO | |
| 66054 | aoskq | WBAR | DBC | EWS | TO | |
| 66055 | aoshkq | WBAR | DBC | DBC | TO | *Alain Thauvette* |
| 66056 | aoshk | WBLE | DBC | EWS | TO | |
| 66057 | aoshk | WBLE | DBC | EWS | TO | |
| 66058 | aoshk | WBAT | GBR | DBS | TO | |
| 66059 | aoshk | WBLE | DBC | EWS | TO | |
| 66060 | aos | WBAT | DBC | EWS | TO | |
| 66061 | aosk | WBAE | DBC | EWS | TO | |
| 66063 | aosk | WBAE | DBC | EWS | TO | |
| 66065 | aoskq | WBAR | DBC | EWS | TO | |
| 66066 | aoskq | WBAR | DBC | DBC | TO | *Geoff Spencer* |
| 66067 | aoskq | WBAR | DBC | EWS | TO | |
| 66068 | aosk | WBAR | DBC | EWS | TO | |
| 66069 | aosq | WBAR | DBC | EWS | TO | |
| 66070 | aos | WBAT | DBC | EWS | TO | |
| 66074 | aosk | WBAE | DBC | EWS | TO | |
| 66075 | aos | WBAT | DBC | EWS | TO | |
| 66076 | aosk | WBAE | DBC | EWS | TO | |
| 66077 | aoskq | WBAR | DBC | EWS | TO | *Benjamin Gimbert G.C.* |
| 66078 | aosk | WBAE | DBC | EWS | TO | |
| 66079 | aosq | WBAR | DBC | EWS | TO | *James Nightall G.C.* |
| 66080 | aosk | WBAE | DBC | EWS | TO | |
| 66081 | aos | WQDA | GBR | EWS | TO (U) | |
| 66082 | aosk | WBAE | DBC | DBC | TO | |
| 66083 | aoskq | WBAR | DBC | EWS | TO | |
| 66084 | aosk | WBAR | DBC | EWS | TO | |
| 66085 | aoskq | WBAR | DBC | DBC | TO | |
| 66086 | aos | WBAT | DBC | EWS | TO | |
| 66087 | aosk | WBAT | DBC | EWS | TO | |
| 66088 | aosk | WBAE | DBC | EWS | TO | |
| 66089 | aoskq | WBAR | DBC | EWS | TO | |
| 66090 | aosk | WBAE | DBC | EWS | TO | |
| 66091 | aosk | WBAR | DBC | EWS | TO | |
| 66092 | aosk | WBAE | DBC | EWS | TO | |
| 66093 | aosk | WBAE | DBC | EWS | TO | |
| 66094 | aosk | WBAE | DBC | EWS | TO | |
| 66095 | aosk | WBAE | DBC | EWS | TO | |
| 66096 | aosk | WBAE | DBC | EWS | TO | |
| 66097 | aosk | WBAE | DBC | DBS | TO | |
| 66098 | aosk | WBAE | DBC | EWS | TO | |
| 66099 | aosrk | WBBE | DBC | EWS | TO | |
| 66100 | aosrk | WBBE | DBC | EWS | TO | |
| 66101 | aosrk | WBBE | DBC | DBS | TO | |
| 66102 | aosrk | WBBE | DBC | EWS | TO | |
| 66103 | aosrk | WBBE | DBC | EWS | TO | |
| 66104 | aosrkq | WBAR | DBC | EWS | TO | |
| 66105 | aosrk | WBBE | DBC | EWS | TO | |

66114 passes Whitley Bridge in North Yorkshire with a train of coal hoppers on 31 March 2017. The loco is in DB Schenker livery which is now being changed to DB Cargo livery. *Pip Dunn*

| | | | | | |
|---|---|---|---|---|---|
| 66106 | aosrk | WBBE | DBC | EWS | TO |
| 66107 | aosrkq | WBAR | DBC | EWS | TO |
| 66108 | aosrk | WBBE | DBC | EWS | TO |
| 66109 | aosq | WBAR | DBC | EWS | TO |
| 66110 | aosrk | WBBE | DBC | EWS | TO |
| 66111 | aosr | WBBT | DBC | EWS | TO |
| 66112 | aosrk | WBBE | DBC | EWS | TO |
| 66113 | aosrk | WBBE | DBC | EWS | TO |
| 66114 | aosrk | WBBE | DBC | DBS | TO |
| 66115 | aos | WBAT | DBC | EWS | TO |
| 66116 | aosk | WBAE | DBC | EWS | TO |
| 66117 | aosk | WBAT | DBC | EWS | TO |
| 66118 | aosk | WBAE | DBC | DBS | TO |
| 66119 | aosk | WBAE | DBC | EWS | TO |
| 66120 | aosk | WBAE | DBC | EWS | TO |
| 66121 | aosk | WBAE | DBC | EWS | TO |
| 66122 | aosk | WBAE | DBC | EWS | TO |
| 66124 | aoskq | WBAR | DBC | DBC | TO |
| 66125 | aosk | WBAE | DBC | EWS | TO |
| 66126 | aosk | WBAE | DBC | EWS | TO |
| 66127 | aos | WBAT | DBC | EWS | TO |
| 66128 | aosk | WBAE | DBC | DBC | TO |
| 66129 | aoskq | WBAR | DBC | EWS | TO |
| 66130 | aoskq | WBAR | DBC | DBC | TO |
| 66131 | aos | WBAT | DBC | EWS | TO |
| 66132 | aosk | WBAT | GBR | EWS | TO |
| 66133 | aosk | WBAE | DBC | EWS | TO |
| 66134 | aosk | WBAE | DBC | EWS | TO |
| 66135 | aosk | WBAE | DBC | EWS | TO |
| 66136 | aoskq | WBAE | DBC | DBC | TO |
| 66137 | aosk | WBAE | DBC | EWS | TO |
| 66138 | aoskq | WBAR | DBC | EWS | TO |

| | | | | | | |
|---|---|---|---|---|---|---|
| 66139 | aosk | WBAE | DBC | EWS | TO | |
| 66140 | aosk | WBAE | DBC | EWS | TO | |
| 66141 | aos | WQDA | GBR | EWS | TO (U) | |
| 66142 | aosk | WBAR | DBC | EWS | TO | |
| 66143 | aosk | WBAE | DBC | EWS | TO | |
| 66144 | aoskq | WBAR | DBC | EWS | TO | |
| 66145 | aosk | WBAE | DBC | EWS | TO | |
| 66147 | aos | WBAT | DBC | EWS | TO | |
| 66148 | aosk | WBAE | DBC | EWS | TO | |
| 66149 | aosk | WBAE | DBC | DBC | TO | |
| 66150 | aosk | WBAE | DBC | DBC | TO | |
| 66151 | aosk | WBAE | DBC | EWS | TO | |
| 66152 | aosk | WBAE | DBC | DBS | TO | *Derek Holmes Railway Operator* |
| 66154 | aosk | WBAE | DBC | EWS | TO | |
| 66155 | aosk | WBAE | DBC | EWS | TO | |
| 66156 | aosk | WBAE | DBC | EWS | TO | |
| 66158 | aosk | WBAE | DBC | EWS | TO | |
| 66160 | aosk | WBAE | DBC | EWS | TO | |
| 66161 | aosk | WBAE | DBC | EWS | TO | |
| 66162 | aosk | WBAR | DBC | EWS | TO | |
| 66164 | aosk | WBAE | DBC | EWS | TO | |
| 66165 | aosq | WBAR | DBC | EWS | TO | |
| 66167 | aosk | WBAE | DBC | EWS | TO | |
| 66168 | aoskq | WBAR | DBC | EWS | TO | |
| 66169 | aos | WBAR | DBC | EWS | TO | |
| 66170 | aosk | WBAE | DBC | EWS | TO | |
| 66171 | aosq | WBAR | DBC | EWS | TO | |
| 66172 | aos | WQAA | DBC | EWS | TO (U) | *PAUL MELLANY* |
| 66174 | aosk | WBAE | DBC | EWS | TO | |
| 66175 | aoskq | WBAE | DBC | EWS | TO | |
| 66176 | aoskq | WBAR | DBC | EWS | TO | |
| 66177 | aos | WBAT | DBC | EWS | TO | |
| 66181 | aosk | WBAE | DBC | EWS | TO | |
| 66182 | aosk | WBAE | DBC | EWS | TO | |
| 66183 | aosk | WBAE | DBC | EWS | TO | |
| 66184 | aos | WBAT | GBR | EWS | TO | |
| 66185 | aosk | WBAE | DBC | DBS | TO | *DP WORLD London Gateway* |
| 66186 | aos | WBAT | DBC | EWS | TO | |
| 66187 | aosk | WBAE | DBC | EWS | TO | |
| 66188 | aoskq | WBAR | DBC | EWS | TO | |
| 66192 | aosk | WBAR | DBC | DBC | TO | |
| 66194 | aoskq | WBAR | DBC | EWS | TO | |
| 66197 | aosk | WBAE | DBC | EWS | TO | |
| 66198 | aoskq | WBAR | DBC | EWS | TO | |
| 66199 | aosk | WBAE | DBC | EWS | TO | |
| 66200 | aosk | WBAE | DBC | EWS | TO | |
| 66206 | aoskq | WBAR | DBC | DBC | TO | |
| 66207 | aosk | WBAE | DBC | EWS | TO | |
| 66221 | aos | WBAT | DBC | EWS | TO | |
| 66230 | aosk | WBAE | DBC | EWS | TO | |
| 66238 | aoskq | WQDA | GBR | EWS | TO | |
| 66250 | aosk | WBAT | GBR | EWS | TO | |

66003-250 have swinghead couplers

66136 has YIWU-LONDON TRAIN branding

66008/016/046/058/081/132/141/184/238/250 have been sold by DB Cargo to GB Railfreight and should be renumbered 66780-789 shortly.

## Class 66/3 – locos ordered by Fastline Freight

Details as per Class 66/0 except:

| | |
|---|---|
| Years introduced: | 2008 |
| Engine Type: | GM 12N-710G3B-T2 |
| Traction Motor type: | GM-EMD D43TRC |
| Fuel tank capacity: | 1,145gal (5,150lit) |

| | | | | | | |
|---|---|---|---|---|---|---|
| 66301 | aosr | XHIM | BEA | DRX | KM | *Kingmoor TMD* |
| 66302 | aosr | XHIM | BEA | DRX | KM | |
| 66303 | aosr | XHIM | BEA | DRX | KM | |
| 66304 | aosr | XHIM | BEA | DRX | KM | |
| 66305 | aosr | XHIM | BEA | DRX | KM | |

## Class 66/4 – locos ordered by DRS

Details as per Class 66/3 except:

| | |
|---|---|
| Years introduced: | 2006-08 |

| | | | | | | |
|---|---|---|---|---|---|---|
| 66413 | aos | DFHJ | MAQ | DRU | LD | |
| 66414 | aos | DFIN | MAQ | FPH | LD | |
| 66415 | aos | DFHJ | MAQ | DRU | LD | |
| 66416 | aos | DFIN | MAQ | FPH | LD | |
| 66418 | aos | DFIN | MAQ | FPH | LD | *PATRIOT – IN MEMORY OF FALLEN RAILWAY EMPLOYEES* |
| 66419 | aos | DFHJ | MAQ | DRU | LD | |
| 66420 | aos | DFIN | MAQ | FPH | LD | |
| 66421 | aos | XHIM | MAQ | DRX | KM | |
| 66422 | aos | XHIM | MAQ | DRX | KM | |
| 66423 | aos | XHIM | MAQ | DRX | KM | |
| 66424 | aos | XHIM | MAQ | DRX | KM | |
| 66425 | aos | XHIM | MAQ | DRX | KM | |
| 66426 | aos | XHIM | MAQ | DRX | KM | |
| 66427 | aos | XHIM | MAQ | DRX | KM | |
| 66428 | aos | XHIM | MAQ | DRX | KM | |
| 66429 | aos | XHIM | MAQ | DRX | KM | |
| 66430 | aos | XHIM | MAQ | DRX | KM | |
| 66431 | aos | XHIM | MAQ | DRX | KM | |
| 66432 | aos | XHIM | MAQ | DRX | KM | |
| 66433 | aos | XHIM | MAQ | DRX | KM | |
| 66434 | aos | XHIM | MAQ | DRX | KM | |

## Class 66/5 – locos ordered by Freightliner

Details for 66501-572 as per Class 66/0, details for 66585-599 as per Class 66/3 except:

| | |
|---|---|
| Years introduced: | 1999-2008 |

| | | | | | | |
|---|---|---|---|---|---|---|
| 66501 | aos | DFIM | POR | FLR | LD | *Japan 2001* |
| 66502 | aos | DFIM | POR | FLR | LD | *Basford Hall Centenary 2001* |
| 66503 | aos | DFIM | POR | FLR | LD | *The RAILWAY MAGAZINE* |
| 66504 | aos | DFIM | POR | FPH | LD | |
| 66505 | aos | DFIM | POR | FLR | LD | |
| 66506 | aos | DFIM | EVS | FLR | LD | *Crewe Regeneration* |
| 66507 | aos | DFHJ | EVS | FLR | LD | |
| 66508 | aos | DFHJ | EVS | FLR | LD | |
| 66509 | aos | DFHH | EVS | FLR | LD | |

| | | | | | | |
|---|---|---|---|---|---|---|
| 66510 | aos | DFHJ | EVS | FLR | LD | |
| 66511 | aos | DFHJ | EVS | FLR | LD | |
| 66512 | aos | DFHH | EVS | FLR | LD | |
| 66513 | aos | DFHJ | EVS | FLR | LD | |
| 66514 | aos | DFHJ | EVS | FLR | LD | |
| 66515 | aos | DFHJ | EVS | FLR | LD | |
| 66516 | aos | DFIM | EVS | FLR | LD | |
| 66517 | aos | DFIM | EVS | FLR | LD | |
| 66518 | aos | DFIM | EVS | FLR | LD | |
| 66519 | aos | DFHH | EVS | FLR | LD | |
| 66520 | aos | DFHH | EVS | FLR | LD | |
| 66522 | aos | DFHH | EVS | FLS | LD | |
| 66523 | aos | DFHH | EVS | FLR | LD | |
| 66524 | aos | DFHJ | EVS | FLR | LD | |
| 66525 | aos | DFHJ | EVS | FLR | LD | |
| 66526 | aos | DFHJ | EVS | FLR | LD | *Driver Steve Dunn (George)* |
| 66528 | aos | DFIM | POR | FPH | LD | *Madge Elliot MBE Borders Railway Opening 2015* |
| 66529 | aos | DFHH | POR | FLR | LD | |
| 66531 | aos | DFHJ | POR | FLR | LD | |
| 66532 | aos | DFIM | POR | FLR | LD | *P&O Nedlloyd Atlas* |
| 66533 | aos | DFIM | POR | FLR | LD | *Hanjin Express/Senator Express* |
| 66534 | aos | DFIM | POR | FLR | LD | *OOCL Express* |
| 66536 | aos | DFIM | POR | FLR | LD | |
| 66537 | aos | DFIM | POR | FLR | LD | |
| 66538 | aos | DFIM | EVS | FLR | LD | |
| 66539 | aos | DFIM | EVS | FLR | LD | |
| 66540 | aos | DFIM | EVS | FLR | LD | *Ruby* |
| 66541 | aos | DFIM | EVS | FLR | LD | |
| 66542 | aos | DFIM | EVS | FLR | LD | |
| 66543 | aos | DFIM | EVS | FLR | LD | |
| 66544 | aos | DFIM | EVS | FLR | LD | |
| 66545 | aos | DFHH | POR | FLR | LD | |
| 66546 | aos | DFHH | POR | FLR | LD | |
| 66547 | aos | DFHH | POR | FLR | LD | |
| 66548 | aos | DFHH | POR | FLR | LD | |
| 66549 | aos | DFHH | POR | FLR | LD | |
| 66550 | aos | DFHH | POR | FLR | LD | |
| 66551 | aos | DFHJ | POR | FLR | LD | |
| 66552 | aos | DFHH | POR | FLR | LD | *Maltby Raider* |
| 66553 | aos | DFHH | POR | FLR | LD | |
| 66554 | aos | DFHH | EVS | FLR | LD | |
| 66555 | aos | DFHH | EVS | FLR | LD | |
| 66556 | aos | DFIM | EVS | FLR | LD | |
| 66557 | aos | DFIM | EVS | FLR | LD | |
| 66558 | aos | DFIM | EVS | FLR | LD | |
| 66559 | aos | DFIM | EVS | FLR | LD | |
| 66560 | aos | DFHH | EVS | FLR | LD | |
| 66561 | aos | DFHH | EVS | FLR | LD | |
| 66562 | aos | DFHH | EVS | FLR | LD | |
| 66563 | aos | DFHJ | EVS | FLR | LD | |
| 66564 | aos | DFHJ | EVS | FLR | LD | |
| 66565 | aos | DFIM | EVS | FLR | LD | |
| 66566 | aos | DFIM | EVS | FLR | LD | |

| | | | | | | |
|---|---|---|---|---|---|---|
| 66567 | aos | DFIM | EVS | FLR | LD | |
| 66568 | aos | DFIM | EVS | FLR | LD | |
| 66569 | aos | DFIM | EVS | FLR | LD | |
| 66570 | aos | DFIM | EVS | FLR | LD | |
| 66571 | aos | DFIM | EVS | FLR | LD | |
| 66572 | aos | DFIM | EVS | FLR | LD | |
| 66585 | aos | DFIN | MAQ | FLR | LD | |
| 66587 | aos | DFIN | MAQ | FLR | LD | |
| 66588 | aos | DFIN | MAQ | FLR | LD | |
| 66589 | aos | DFIN | MAQ | FLR | LD | |
| 66590 | aos | DFIN | MAQ | FLR | LD | |
| 66591 | aos | DFIN | MAQ | FLR | LD | |
| 66592 | aos | DFIN | MAQ | FLR | LD | *Johnson Stevens Agencies* |
| 66593 | aos | DFIN | MAQ | FLR | LD | *3MG MERSEY MULTIMODAL GATEWAY* |
| 66594 | aos | DFIN | MAQ | FLR | LD | *NYK Spirit of Kyoto* |
| 66595 | aos | DFIN | BEA | FLR | LD | |
| 66596 | aos | DFGH | BEA | FLR | LD | |
| 66597 | aos | DFGH | BEA | FLR | LD | *Viridor* |
| 66598 | aos | DFHG | BEA | FLR | LD | |
| 66599 | aos | DFHG | BEA | FLR | LD | |

## Class 66/6 – regeared locos ordered by Freightliner

Details for 66601-622 as per Class 66/0, details for 66623 as per Class 66/3 except:

| | |
|---|---|
| Years introduced: | 2000-07 |
| Maximum tractive effort: | 105,080lbf (467kN) |
| Continuous tractive effort: | 66,630lbf (296kN) |
| Maximum design speed: | 65mph (104km/h) |

| | | | | | | |
|---|---|---|---|---|---|---|
| 66601 | aos | DFHH | POR | FLR | LD | *The Hope Valley* |
| 66602 | aos | DFHH | POR | FLR | LD | |
| 66603 | aos | DFHH | POR | FLR | LD | |
| 66604 | aos | DFHH | POR | FLR | LD | |
| 66605 | aos | DFHH | POR | FLR | LD | |
| 66606 | aos | DFHH | POR | FLR | LD | |
| 66607 | aos | DFHH | POR | FLR | LD | |
| 66610 | aos | DFHH | POR | FLR | LD | |
| 66613 | aos | DFHH | EVS | FLR | LD | |
| 66614 | aos | DFHH | EVS | FLR | LD | *1916 POPPY 2016* |
| 66615 | aos | DFHH | EVS | FLR | LD | |
| 66617 | aos | DFHH | EVS | FLR | LD | |
| 66618 | aos | DFHH | EVS | FLR | LD | *Railways Illustrated Annual Photographic Awards Alan Barnes* |
| 66619 | aos | DFHH | EVS | FLR | LD | *Derek W. Johnson MBE* |
| 66620 | aos | DFHH | EVS | FLR | LD | |
| 66621 | aos | DFHH | EVS | FLR | LD | |
| 66622 | aos | DFHH | EVS | FLR | LD | |
| 66623 | aos | DFHH | MAQ | BAF | LD | *Bill Bolsover* |

## Class 66/7 – locos ordered or acquired by GB Railfreight

Details for 66701-751 as per Class 66/0, details for 66752-779 as per Class 66/3 except:

| | |
|---|---|
| Years introduced: | 2001-16 |
| Engine: | EMD 12N-710G3B-T2 (66718-732/747-749) |
| Traction Motor type: | GM-EMD D43TRC (66718-732/747-749) |
| Fuel tank capacity: | 1,440gal (6,550lit) 66701-717/733-746/750/751, 1,220gal (5,546lit) – 66718-722, 1,312gal (5,150lit) – 66723-732/747-749/752-779 |

| | | | | | | | |
|---|---|---|---|---|---|---|---|
| 66701 | | aos | GBBT | EVS | GBO | RR | |
| 66702 | | aos | GBBT | EVS | GBR | RR | *Blue Lightning* |
| 66703 | | aos | GBBT | EVS | GBR | RR | *Doncaster PSB 1981-2002* |
| 66704 | | aos | GBBT | EVS | GBR | RR | *Colchester Power Signalbox* |
| 66705 | | aos | GBBT | EVS | GBR | RR | *Golden Jubilee* |
| 66706 | | aos | GBBT | EVS | GBR | RR | *Nene Valley* |
| 66707 | | aos | GBBT | EVS | GBR | RR | *Sir Sam Fay* |
| 66708 | | aos | GBBT | EVS | GBR | RR | *Jayne* |
| 66709 | | aos | GBBT | EVS | MSC | RR | *Sorrento* |
| 66710 | | aos | GBBT | EVS | GBR | RR | *Phil Packer BRIT* |
| 66711 | | aos | GBBT | EVS | AGI | RR | *Sence* |
| 66712 | | aos | GBBT | EVS | GBR | RR | *Peterborough Power Signalbox* |
| 66713 | | aos | GBBT | EVS | GBR | RR | *Forest City* |
| 66714 | | aos | GBBT | EVS | GBR | RR | *Cromer Lifeboats* |
| 66715 | | aos | GBBT | EVS | GBR | RR | *VALOUR* |
| 66716 | | aos | GBBT | EVS | GBR | RR | *LOCOMOTIVE & CARRIAGE INSTITUTION CENTENARY 1911-2011* |
| 66717 | | aos | GBBT | EVS | GBR | RR | *Good Old Boy* |
| 66718 | | aos | GBLT | EVS | LUB | RR | *Sir Peter Hendy CBE* |
| 66719 | | aos | GBLT | EVS | GBR | RR | *METRO-LAND* |
| 66720 | | aos | GBLT | EVS | EMY | RR | |
| 66721 | | aos | GBLT | EVS | LUW | RR | *Harry Beck* |
| 66722 | | aos | GBLT | EVS | GBR | RR | *Sir Edward Watkin* |
| 66723 | | aos | GBLT | EVS | GBZ | RR | *Chinook* |
| 66724 | | aos | GBLT | EVS | GBF | RR | *Drax Power Station* |
| 66725 | | aos | GBLT | EVS | GBZ | RR | *SUNDERLAND* |
| 66726 | | aos | GBLT | EVS | GBF | RR | *SHEFFIELD WEDNESDAY* |
| 66727 | | aos | GBLT | EVS | MRT | RR | *Maritime One* |
| 66728 | | aos | GBLT | EVS | GBR | RR | *Institution of Railway Operators* |
| 66729 | | aos | GBLT | EVS | GBR | RR | *DERBY COUNTY* |
| 66730 | | aos | GBLT | EVS | GBR | RR | *Whitemoor* |
| 66731 | | aos | GBLT | EVS | GBR | RR | *InterhubGB* |
| 66732 | | aos | GBLT | EVS | GBR | RR | *GBRF The First Decade 1999-2009 John Smith MD* |
| 66733 | 66401 | aosr | GBFM | POR | GBR | RR | *Cambridge PSB* |
| 66735 | 66403 | aosr | GBBT | POR | GBR | RR | |
| 66736 | 66404 | aosr | GBFM | POR | GBR | RR | *WOLVERHAMPTON WANDERERS* |
| 66737 | 66405 | aosr | GBFM | POR | GBR | RR | *Lesia* |
| 66738 | 66578 | aos | GBBT | BEA | GBR | RR | *HUDDERSFIELD TOWN* |
| 66739 | 66579 | aos | GBFM | BEA | GBR | RR | *Bluebell Railway* |
| 66740 | 66580 | aosr | GBFM | BEA | GBR | RR | *Sarah* |
| 66741 | 66581 | aos | GBBT | BEA | GBR | RR | *Swanage Railway* |

| | | | | | | | |
|---|---|---|---|---|---|---|---|
| 66742 | 66406, 66841 | aos | GBBT | BEA | GBR | RR | *ABP Port of Immingham Centenary 1912-2012* |
| 66743 | 66407, 66842 | aosr | GBFM | BEA | ROY | RR | |
| 66744 | 66408, 66843 | aos | GBBT | BEA | GBR | RR | *Crossrail* |
| 66745 | 66409, 66844 | aos | GBRT | BEA | GBR | RR | *Modern Railways The first 50 years* |
| 66746 | 66410, 66845 | aostr | GBFM | BEA | ROY | RR | |
| 66747 | | aos | GBEB | GBR | GBR | RR | |
| 66748 | | aos | GBEB | GBR | GBR | RR | *West Burton 50* |
| 66749 | | aos | GBEB | GBR | GBR | RR | |
| 66750 | | aos | GBEB | BEA | GBR | RR | *Bristol Panel Signal Box* |
| 66751 | | aos | GBEB | BEA | GBR | RR | *Inspirational Delivered Hitachi Rail Europe* |
| 66752 | | aos | GBEL | GBR | GBR | RR | *The Hoosier State* |
| 66753 | | aos | GBEL | GBR | GBR | RR | *EMD Roberts Road* |
| 66754 | | aos | GBEL | GBR | GBR | RR | *Northampton Saints* |
| 66755 | | aos | GBEL | GBR | GBR | RR | |
| 66756 | | aos | GBEL | GBR | GBR | RR | *Royal Corps of Signals* |
| 66757 | | aos | GBEL | GBR | GBR | RR | *West Somerset Railway* |
| 66758 | | aos | GBEL | GBR | GBR | RR | |
| 66759 | | aos | GBEL | GBR | GBR | RR | *Chippy* |
| 66760 | | aos | GBEL | GBR | GBR | RR | *David Gordon Harris* |
| 66761 | | aos | GBEL | GBR | GBR | RR | *Wensleydale Railway Association 25 Years 1990-2015* |
| 66762 | | aos | GBEL | GBR | GBR | RR | |
| 66763 | | aos | GBEL | GBR | GBR | RR | *Severn Valley Railway* |
| 66764 | | aos | GBEL | GBR | GBR | RR | |
| 66765 | | aos | GBEL | GBR | GBR | RR | |
| 66766 | | aos | GBEL | GBR | GBR | RR | |
| 66767 | | aos | GBEL | GBR | GBR | RR | |
| 66768 | | aos | GBEL | GBR | GBR | RR | |
| 66769 | | aos | GBEL | GBR | GBR | RR | |
| 66770 | | aos | GBEL | GBR | GBR | RR | |
| 66771 | | aos | GBEL | GBR | GBR | RR | |
| 66772 | | aos | GBEL | GBR | GBR | RR | |
| 66773 | | aos | GBNB | GBR | GBR | RR | |
| 66774 | | aos | GBNB | GBR | GBR | RR | |
| 66775 | | aos | GBNB | GBR | GBZ | RR | *HMS Argyll* |
| 66776 | | aos | GBNB | GBR | GBR | RR | *Joanne* |
| 66777 | | aos | GBNB | GBR | GBR | RR | *Annette* |
| 66778 | | aos | GBNB | GBR | GBR | RR | *Darius Cheskin* |
| 66779 | | aos | GBEL | GBR | GYP | RR | *EVENING STAR* |

Note: 66723 carries ZA723 as well as its TOPS number

Note: 66775 carries F231 as well as its TOPS number

## Class 66/8 – locos acquired by Colas Rail Freight

Details as per Class 66/0 except:

Years introduced: 2003/04 (as 66/5s)

Fuel tank capacity: 1,440gal (6,550lit)

| | | | | | | | |
|---|---|---|---|---|---|---|---|
| 66846 | 66573 | aost | COLO | COL | COL | RU | |
| 66847 | 66574 | aost | COLO | COL | COL | RU | |
| 66848 | 66575 | aost | COLO | COL | COL | RU | |
| 66849 | 66576 | aost | COLO | COL | COL | RU | *Wylam Dilly* |
| 66850 | 66577 | aost | COLO | COL | COL | RU | *David Maidment OBE* |

GB Railfreight's 66738 *Huddersfield Town* passes East Garforth with 6D72, the 1132 Hull-Rylstone, on 28 April 2017. This is one of five locos named after football clubs in the GBRf fleet. *Anthony Hicks*

## Class 66/9 – low emission locos ordered by Freightliner

Details as per Class 66/3 except:

| | |
|---|---|
| Years introduced: | 2004/08 |
| Fuel tank capacity: | 1,224gal (5,510lit); t – 1,312gal (5,905lit) |

| | | | | | | |
|---|---|---|---|---|---|---|
| 66951 | aost | DFIN | EVS | FLR | LD | |
| 66952 | aos | DFHG | EVS | FLR | LD | |
| 66953 | aos | DFHJ | BEA | FLR | LD | |
| 66954 | aos | DFIN | BEA | FLR | LD | |
| 66955 | aos | DFIN | BEA | FLR | LD | |
| 66956 | aos | DFIN | BEA | FLR | LD | |
| 66957 | aos | DFHG | BEA | FLR | LD | *Stephenson Locomotive Society 1909-2009* |

---

## Class 67

*Essentially a Bo-Bo, ETH fitted 125mph mixed traffic version of the Class 66, 30 locos were ordered by EWS and delivered in 1999-2000. Two have since been sold to Colas Rail Freight, but reducing work means several are withdrawn.*

| | |
|---|---|
| Built by: | Alstom/General Motors, Valencia, Spain |
| Years introduced: | 1999-2000 |
| Wheel arrangement: | Bo-Bo |
| Weight: | 90 tons |
| Length: | 64ft 7in (19.71m) |
| Engine Type: | GM 12N-710G3B-EC |
| Engine output: | 2,980hp (2,223kW) |

| | |
|---|---|
| Power at rail | 2,493hp (1,860kW) |
| Maximum tractive effort: | 31,750lbf (141kN) |
| Continuous tractive effort: | 20,200lbf (90kN) |
| ETH index: | 66 |
| Maximum design speed: | 125mph (200km/h) restricted to 110mph (177km/h) |
| Brake Force | 78 tons |
| Route Availability: | 8 |
| Traction alternator: | GM-EMD AR9A |
| Companion alternator: | GM-EMD CA6HEX |
| Traction Motor type: | GM-EMD D43FM |
| Fuel tank capacity | 1,095gal (4,927lit) |
| Multiple Working type: | AAR |

| | | | | | | |
|---|---|---|---|---|---|---|
| 67001 | aep | WQAA | DBC | ATW | TO (S) | |
| 67002 | aep | WAAC | DBC | ATW | CE | |
| 67003 | aep | WAAC | DBC | ATW | CE | |
| 67004 | aepr | WQAA | DBC | CAL | TO (S) | *Cairn Gorm* |
| 67005 | aep | WAAC | DBC | RTO | CE | *Queen's Messenger* |
| 67006 | aep | WAAC | DBC | RTO | CE | *Royal Sovereign* |
| 67007 | aepr | WABC | DBC | EWS | CE | |
| 67008 | aep | WAAC | DBC | EWS | CE | |
| 67009 | aepr | WQAA | DBC | EWS | CE (S) | |
| 67010 | aep | WAAC | DBC | DBC | CE | |
| 67011 | aepr | WQAB | DBC | EWS | CE (S) | |
| 67012 | aep | WAAC | DBC | CRS | CE | |

DB Cargo 67013 leads 1S25, the 2116 Euston-Inverness Caledonian sleeper, past Cuaich, just north of Dalwhinnie, on the Highland Main Line on 9 May 2017. *Anthony Hicks*

| | | | | | | |
|---|---|---|---|---|---|---|
| 67013 | aep | WAAC | DBC | DBC | CE | |
| 67014 | aep | WAAC | DBC | CRS | CE | |
| 67015 | aep | WAWC | DBC | CRS | CE | |
| 67016 | aep | WAWC | DBC | EWS | CE | |
| 67017 | aep | WQAB | DBC | EWS | CE (S) | *Arrow* |
| 67018 | aep | WAWC | DBC | DBS | CE | *Keith Heller* |
| 67019 | aep | WQBA | DBC | EWS | TO (U) | |
| 67020 | aep | WAAC | DBC | EWS | CE | |
| 67021 | aep | WAAC | DBC | PUL | CE | |
| 67022 | aep | WAAC | DBC | EWS | CE | |
| 67023 | aep | COFS | COL | COL | RU | *Charlotte* |
| 67024 | aep | WAAC | DBC | PUL | CE | |
| 67025 | aep | WQBA | DBC | EWS | CE (U) | *Western Star* |
| 67026 | aep | WQAB | DBC | JUB | CE (S) | *Diamond Jubilee* |
| 67027 | aep | COFS | COL | COL | RU | *Stella* |
| 67028 | aep | WAAC | DBC | DBC | CE | |
| 67029 | aepq | WACC | DBC | DBM | CE | *Royal Diamond* |
| 67030 | aepr | WABC | DBC | EWS | CE | |

67010 has 'First choice for rail freight in the UK' branding
67028 has 'Leading the next generation of rail freight' branding
67001-030 have swinghead couplers

## Class 68

*New mixed traffic Bo-Bo loco ordered by DRS in 2012. Initial order for 15 upped to 25, then 32 and presently 34 locos. More could be ordered. 68019-032 will be dedicated for Transpennine use (these are currently being modified and re-liveried) whilst 68010-015 are dedicated to Chiltern Railways services, with 68008/009 as additional cover locos.*

| | |
|---|---|
| Built by: | Vossloh/Stadler, Valencia |
| Years introduced: | 2014-17 |
| Wheel arrangement: | Bo-Bo |
| Weight: | 85 tons |
| Length: | 20.5m |
| Engine Type: | Caterpillar C175-16 |
| Engine output: | 3,805hp (2,839kW) |
| Power at rail | 3,190hp (2,380kW) |
| Tractive effort: | 71,260lbf (317kN) |
| Continuous tractive effort: | 56,200lbf (250kN) |
| ETH index: | 96 |
| Maximum design speed: | 100mph (160km/h) |
| Brake Force: | 73 tons |
| Route Availability: | 7 |
| Main alternator type: | ABB WGX560 |
| Traction Motor type: | ABB 4FRA6063 |
| Fuel tank capacity: | 1,120gal (5,600lit) |
| Multiple Working type: | within class and Class 88 only |

| | | | | | | |
|---|---|---|---|---|---|---|
| 68001 | aep* | XHVE | BEA | DRN | CR | *Evolution* |
| 68002 | aep* | XHVE | BEA | DRN | CR | *Intrepid* |
| 68003 | aep* | XHVE | BEA | DRN | CR | *Astute* |
| 68004 | aep* | XHVE | BEA | DRN | CR | *Rapid* |
| 68005 | aep* | XHVE | BEA | DRN | CR | *Defiant* |
| 68006 | aep* | XHVE | BEA | SCR | CR | *Daring* |

DRS 68009 *Titan* passes Gosberton, near Spalding, with a train of Railhead Treatment Trains vehicles heading for use in East Anglia on September 9 2014. This loco is one of eight mainly used by Chiltern Railways. *Pip Dunn*

| | | | | | | |
|---|---|---|---|---|---|---|
| 68007 | aep* | XHVE | BEA | SCR | CR | *Valiant* |
| 68008 | aeup* | XHVE | BEA | DRN | CR | *Avenger* |
| 68009 | aeup* | XHVE | BEA | DRN | CR | *Titan* |
| 68010 | aeup* | XHCE | BEA | CRS | CR | *Oxford Flyer* |
| 68011 | aeup* | XHCE | BEA | CRS | CR | |
| 68012 | aeup* | XHCE | BEA | CRS | CR | |
| 68013 | aeup* | XHCE | BEA | CRS | CR | |
| 68014 | aeup* | XHCE | BEA | CRS | CR | |
| 68015 | aeup* | XHCE | BEA | CRS | CR | |
| 68016 | aep* | XHVE | BEA | DRN | CR | *Fearless* |
| 68017 | aep* | XHVE | BEA | DRN | CR | *Hornet* |
| 68018 | aep* | XHVE | BEA | DRN | CR | *Vigilant* |
| 68019 | aeup* | XHTP | BEA | TPE | CR | *Brutus* |
| 68020 | aeup* | XHTP | BEA | DRN | CR | *Reliance* |
| 68021 | aeup* | XHTP | BEA | TPE | CR | *Tireless* |
| 68022 | aeup* | XHTP | BEA | DRN | CR | *Resolution* |
| 68023 | aeup* | XHTP | BEA | DRN | BH (S) | *Achilles* |
| 68024 | aeup* | XHTP | BEA | DRN | BH (S) | *Centaur* |
| 68025 | aeup* | XHTP | BEA | DRN | BH (S) | *Superb* |
| 68026 | aep* | XHTP | BEA | DRX | CR | |
| 68027 | aep* | XHTP | BEA | DRX | CR | |
| 68028 | aep* | XHVE | BEA | DRX | CR | |
| 68029 | aep* | XHVE | BEA | DRX | CR | |
| 68030 | aep* | XHVE | BEA | DRX | CR | |
| 68031 | aep* | XHVE | BEA | DRX | CR | |
| 68032 | aep* | XHVE | BEA | DRX | CR | |
| 68033 | aep* | XHVE | BEA | DRN | CR | |
| 68034 | aep* | XHVE | BEA | DRN | CR | |

Note: XHVE/XHCE and XHTP locos have different push pull systems and are not interoperable between the pools.

68019-032 will all move to XHTP

## Class 70

*General Electric freight loco design ordered by Freightliner. The initial order was for 20 locos with an option for ten more, which was not taken up. Instead those locos were taken by Colas Rail Freight which later ordered seven more.*

*Freightliner's 70012 was delivered to the UK but badly damaged when it was dropped by the crane during unloading, so it was returned to the USA and is deemed as disposed.*

*70801 was formerly a demonstrator loco numbered 70099 which was built from a kit delivered to Turkey and shipped to the UK before being taken on by Colas.*

| | |
|---|---|
| Built by: | General Electric, Erie, Pennsylvania |
| Years introduced: | 2009-12 |
| Wheel arrangement: | Co-Co |
| Weight: | 129 tons |
| Length: | 21.71m |
| Engine Type: | GE Powerhaul P616LDA1 |
| Engine output: | 3,820hp (2,848kW) |
| Power at rail: | 2,700hp (2,014kW) |
| Tractive effort: | 122,000lbf (544kN) |
| Continuous tractive effort | 96,000lbf (427kN) |
| Maximum design speed: | 75mph (120km/h) |
| Brake Force: | 96.7 tons |
| Route Availability: | 7 |
| Main alternator type: | GE 5GTAZ6721A1 |
| Traction Motor type: | AC-GE 5GEB30B |
| Fuel tank capacity: | 1,333gal (6,000lit) |
| Multiple Working type: | AAR |

## Class 70/0 – Freightliner Locos

| | | | | | | |
|---|---|---|---|---|---|---|
| 70001 | aos | DHLT | MAQ | FPH | LD (U) | *PowerHaul* |
| 70002 | aos | DHLT | MAQ | FPH | LD (U) | |
| 70003 | aos | DFGI | MAQ | FPH | LD | |
| 70004 | aos | DFGI | MAQ | FPH | LD | *The Coal Industry Society* |
| 70005 | aos | DFGI | MAQ | FPH | LD | |
| 70006 | aos | DFGI | MAQ | FPH | LD | |
| 70007 | aos | DFGI | MAQ | FPH | LD | |
| 70008 | aos | DFGI | MAQ | FPH | LD | |
| 70009 | aos | DHLT | MAQ | FPH | LD (U) | |
| 70010 | aos | DFGI | MAQ | FPH | LD | |
| 70011 | aos | DFGI | MAQ | FPH | LD | |
| 70013 | aos | DHLT | MAQ | FPH | LD (U) | |
| 70014 | aos | DFGI | MAQ | FPH | LD | |
| 70015 | aos | DFGI | MAQ | FPH | LD | |
| 70016 | aos | DHLT | MAQ | FPH | LD (U) | |
| 70017 | aos | DFGI | MAQ | FPH | LD | |
| 70018 | aos | DHLT | MAQ | FPH | LD (U) | |
| 70019 | aos | DFGI | MAQ | FPH | LD | |
| 70020 | aos | DFGI | MAQ | FPH | LD | |

Freightliner's 70013 works an Ellesmere Port-Fiddlers Ferry coal train past Monks Siding on 24 March 2012.
*Anthony Hicks*

## Class 70/8 – Colas Rail Freight locos

Details as per Class 70/0

| | | | | | | |
|---|---|---|---|---|---|---|
| 70801 | 70099 | aos | COLO | LOM | COL | CF |
| 70802 | | aos | COLO | LOM | COL | CF |
| 70803 | | aos | COLO | LOM | COL | CF |
| 70804 | | aos | COLO | LOM | COL | CF |
| 70805 | | aos | COLO | LOM | COL | CF |
| 70806 | | aos | COLO | LOM | COL | CF |
| 70807 | | aos | COLO | LOM | COL | CF |
| 70808 | | aos | COLO | LOM | COL | CF |
| 70809 | | aos | COLO | LOM | COL | CF |
| 70810 | | aos | COLO | LOM | COL | CF |
| 70811 | | aos | COLO | LOM | COL | CF |
| 70812 | | aos | COLO | LOM | COL | CF |
| 70813 | | aos | COLO | LOM | COL | CF |
| 70814 | | aos | COLO | LOM | COL | CF |
| 70815 | | aos | COLO | LOM | COL | CF |
| 70816 | | aos | COLO | LOM | COL | CF |
| 70817 | | aos | COLO | LOM | COL | CF |

## Class 73

*A fleet of six prototype Electro Diesel locos (Class 73/0) were built in 1962 by BR at Eastleigh followed by a production series of 43 locos (Class 73/1) built by EE at Vulcan Foundry in 1965. In 1988, 12, later increased to 14, locos were modified for dedicated Gatwick Express use (Class 73/2) while two 73/0s were converted for Sandite use on Merseyrail as Class 73/9s.*

*Two re-engineering programmes have recently been undertaken, one by RVEL (now LORAM) at Derby for Network Rail which saw the EE diesel engine replaced by two Cummins engines. Only two locos have been modified.*

*Brush also rebuilt 11 locos for GBRf with single MTU engines. Five of these are for NR contacts (73961-965) while the other six (73966-971) are dedicated for Caledonian Sleeper work in Scotland. There are a few differences between these two fleets. More GBRf conversions may be forthcoming and the company still retains a sizeable fleet of original 73s still in main line use.*

| | |
|---|---|
| Built by: | English Electric, Vulcan Foundry |
| Years introduced: | 1962-67 |
| Wheel arrangement: | Bo-Bo |
| Weight: | 76-77 tons |
| Length: | 53ft 8in (16.96m) |
| Power supply: | 750V DC third rail |
| Engine Type: | English Electric 4SRKT Mk 2 |
| Engine output: | 600hp (447kW) |
| Electric output: | 1,600hp (1,193kW) |
| Power at rail (diesel): | 402hp (300kW) |
| Electric power at rail (Cont): | 1,200hp (895kW) |
| Electric power at rail (Max): | 2,450hp (1,830kW) |
| Electric tractive effort: | 40,000lb (179kN) – Electric |
| Diesel tractive effort: | 36,000lbf (160kN) – Diesel |
| Continuous tractive effort | 13,600lbf (60kN) – Diesel |
| ETH index: | 38 on electric power only |
| Maximum design speed: | 90mph (144km/h) |
| Brake Force: | 31 tons |
| Route Availability: | 6 |
| Main generator type: | EE824-3D |
| Auxiliary generator type: | EE908-3C |
| Traction Motor type: | EE546-1B |
| Fuel tank capacity: | 310gal (1,409lit) |
| Multiple Working type: | Blue Star |

GBRf is the biggest user of Class 73s, and still has several original Class 73/1s in regular main line use. 73136 *Mhairi* stands at Sheffield Park on 16 April 2016. *Pip Dunn*

## Class 73/1: standard locos

| | | | | | | | |
|---|---|---|---|---|---|---|---|
| 73107 | E6013 | xew | GBED | GBR | GBR | SE | *Tracy* |
| 73109 | E6015 | xew | GBED | GBR | GBR | SE | |
| 73110 | E6016 | xew | GBED | GBR | EBY | ZG (S) | |
| 73119 | E6025 | xew | GBED | GBR | GBR | SE | *Borough of Eastleigh* |
| 73128 | E6035 | xew | GBED | GBR | GBR | SE | *OVS BULLEID CBE* |
| 73134 | E6041 | xew | GBBR | GBR | ICO | BL (U) | |
| 73136 | E6043 | xew | GBED | GBR | GBR | SE | *Mhairi* |
| 73138 | E6045 | aew | QADD | NET | NRY | SE | |
| 73141 | E6048 | xew | GBED | GBR | GBR | SE | *Charlotte* |
| 73201 | E6049, 73142 | aew | GBED | GBR | BRB | SE | *Broadlands* |
| 73202 | E6044, 73137 | aew | MBED | POR | SOU | SL | *Graham Stenning* |
| 73212 | E6008, 73102 | aewp* | GBED | GBR | GBR | SE | *Fiona* |
| 73213 | E6018, 73112 | aewp* | GBED | GBR | GBR | SE | *Rhodalyn* |
| 73235 | E6042, 73135 | aew | HYWD | POR | SWU | BM | |

Note: 73212/213 have snowplough brackets at one end only

## Class 73/9 – LORAM rebuilt locos

Details as per Class 73/1 except:

| | |
|---|---|
| Built by: | LORAM |
| Years introduced: | 2015 |
| Engine type | two Cummins QSK19 |
| Engine output (total): | 1,500hp (1,119kW) |
| Power at rail (diesel): | 1,005hp (750kW) |
| Electric tractive effort: | 40,000lbf (179kN) |
| Diesel tractive effort: | 40,000lbf (179kN) |
| Maximum design speed: | 90mph |
| Brake Force: | 31 tonnes |
| Fuel tank capacity: | 500gal (2,260lit) |
| Multiple Working type: | AAR |

| | | | | | | | |
|---|---|---|---|---|---|---|---|
| 73951 | E6010, 73104 | ao | QADD | NET | NRY | ZA | *Malcolm Brinded* |
| 73952 | E6019, 73113, 73211 | ao | QADD | NET | NRY | ZA | *Janis Kong* |

Network Rail has had two Class 73s rebuilt by LORAM with pairs of Cummins engines replacing their EE units. 73951/952 stand at Bewdley during a visit to the Severn Valley Railway on 20 May 2016. *Pip Dunn*

GBRf has 11 Class 73s rebuilt with MTU engines, with six dedicated to working Caledonian Sleeper trains. 73968 works an Oban-Polmadie empty stock train past Dalrigh, between Tyndum Lower and Crianlarich, on 25 March 2017. *Anthony Hicks*

## Class 73/9 – Brush rebuilt locos

Details as per Class 73/1 except:

| | |
|---|---|
| Built by: | Brush Loughborough |
| Years introduced: | 2014-15 |
| Engine type | MTU R4000L 8V43 |
| Engine output: | 1,600hp (1,194kW) |
| Power at rail (diesel): | 1,072hp (800kW) |
| ETH index: | 50 (73961-965), 90 (73966-971) |
| Maximum design speed: | 90mph |
| Brake Force: | 31 tonnes |
| Main alternator type: | Lechmotoren SDV 87.53-12 |
| Multiple Working type: | Blue Star and AAR |

| | | | | | | | |
|---|---|---|---|---|---|---|---|
| 73961 | E6026, 73120, 73209 | aetwp | GBNR | GBR | GBR | SE | *Alison* |
| 73962 | E6032, 73125, 73204 | aetwp | GBNR | GBR | GBR | SE | *Dick Mabbutt* |
| 73963 | E6030, 73123, 73206 | aetwp | GBNR | GBR | GBR | SE | *Janice* |
| 73964 | E6031, 73124, 73205 | aetwp | GBNR | GBR | GBR | SE | *Jeanette* |
| 73965 | E6028, 73121, 73208 | aetwp | GBNR | GBR | GBR | SE | |
| 73966 | E6005, 73005 | aetrdp* | GBCS | GBR | CAL | EC | |
| 73967 | E6006, 73006, 73906 | aetrdp* | GBCS | GBR | CAL | EC | |
| 73968 | E6023, 73117 | aetrdp* | GBCS | GBR | CAL | EC | |
| 73969 | E6011, 73105 | aetrdp* | GBCS | GBR | CAL | EC | |
| 73970 | E6009, 73103 | aetrdp* | GBCS | GBR | CAL | EC | |
| 73971 | E6029, 73122, 73207 | aetrdp* | GBCS | GBR | CAL | EC | |

Note: 73962/964 have cab end brackets for fitting ladders for working on the East London Line.
The 750V DC capability on 73966-971 is currently isolated

## Class 86

*The standard 25kV AC loco built for BR in the mid-1960s, totalling 100 examples. 61 were modified to Class 86/2s, while the remaining Class 86/0s were later changed to either Class 86/3s or 86/4s, with the 86/3s duly becoming 86/4s. Of the 39 Class 86/4s, 30 were converted to freight only Class 86/6s, 16 of which remain in traffic with Freightliner.*

*Several Class 86/2s have been exported for use in Bulgaria and Hungary.*

| | |
|---|---|
| Built by: | English Electric Vulcan Foundry and BR Doncaster |
| Years introduced: | 1965-66 |
| Wheel arrangement: | Bo-Bo |
| Weight: | 83-87 tons |
| Length: | 58ft 6in (17.83m) |
| Power supply | 25kV AC |
| Control system: | HT tap changing |
| Traction output (max): | 7,680hp (5,860kW) |
| Traction output (cont.): | 5,000hp (3,730kW) |
| Tractive effort: | 58,000lb (258kN) |
| ETH index: | 74 |
| Maximum design speed: | 100-110mph (160-180km/h) |
| Brake Force: | 40 tons |
| Route Availability: | 6 |
| Traction Motor type: | GEC G412AZ |
| Multiple Working type: | TDM |

## Class 86/1 – test locos

| | | | | | | | |
|---|---|---|---|---|---|---|---|
| 86101 | E3191, 86201 | xe | GBCH | ACL | CAL | WN | *Sir William A Stanier FRS* |

## Class 86/2 – standard locos

Details as per Class 86/1 except:

| | |
|---|---|
| Traction output (max): | 6,100hp (4,550kW) |
| Traction output (cont.): | 4,040hp (3,013kW) |
| Traction Motor type: | AEI 282AZ |

| | | | | | | | |
|---|---|---|---|---|---|---|---|
| 86259 | E3137, 86045 | xe | GROG | LES | EBY | WN | *Les Ross* |

## Class 86/4 – regeared locos

Details as per Class 86/1 except:

| | |
|---|---|
| Traction output (max): | 5,900hp (4,400kW) |
| Traction output (cont.): | 3,600hp (2,680kW) |
| Traction Motor type: | AEI 282AZ |

| | | | | | | | |
|---|---|---|---|---|---|---|---|
| 86401 | E3199, 86001 | xe | GBCH | ACL | CAL | WN | *Mons Meg* |

## Class 86/6 – freight only locos

Details as per Class 86/1 except:

| | |
|---|---|
| Traction output (max): | 5,900hp (4,400kW) |
| Traction output (cont.): | 3,600hp (2,680kW) |
| Maximum design speed: | 75mph (120km/h) |
| Traction Motor type: | AEI 282AZ |
| No train heating | |

Freightliner's 86637 and 86610 work a diverted Tilbury-Coatbridge intermodal train through York on 19 July 2013. The locos sport different liveries - the new 'Powerhaul' livery and the previous green and yellow. *Anthony Hicks*

| | | | | | | |
|---|---|---|---|---|---|---|
| 86604 | E3103, 86004, 86404 | aym | DFNC | FLI | FLH | CB |
| 86605 | E3185, 86005, 86405 | aym | DFNC | FLI | FLH | CB |
| 86607 | E3176, 86007, 86407 | aym | DFNC | FLI | FLH | CB |
| 86608 | E3180, 86008, 86408, 86501 | aym | DFNC | FLI | FLH | CB |
| 86609 | E3102, 86009, 86409 | aym | DFNC | FLI | FLH | CB |
| 86610 | E3104, 86010, 86410 | aym | DFNC | FLI | FLH | CB |
| 86612 | E3122, 86012, 86312, 86412 | aym | DFNC | POR | FLH | CB |
| 86613 | E3128, 86013, 86313, 86413 | aym | DFNC | POR | FLH | CB |
| 86614 | E3145, 86014, 86314, 86414 | aym | DFNC | POR | FLH | CB |
| 86622 | E3174, 86022, 86322, 86422 | aym | DFNC | POR | FPH | CB |
| 86627 | E3110, 86027, 86327, 86427 | aym | DFNC | POR | FLH | CB |
| 86628 | E3159, 86028, 86328, 86428 | aym | DFNC | POR | FLH | CB |
| 86632 | E3148, 86032, 86432 | aym | DFNC | POR | FLH | CB |
| 86637 | E3130, 86037, 86437 | aym | DFNC | POR | FPH | CB |
| 86638 | E3108, 86038, 86438 | aym | DFNC | POR | FLH | CB |
| 86639 | E3153, 86039, 86439 | aym | DFNC | POR | FLH | CB |

Privately-owned but on hire to GB Railfreight for working Caledonian Sleeper trains, 87002 *Royal Sovereign* is stabled at Edinburgh Waverley on 10 September 2016. *Pip Dunn*

## Class 87

*An improved version of the Class 86, 36 locos were built from 1973 for the newly electrified northern section of the WCML. The last of the class were withdrawn by Virgin Trains in the early 2000s. Several have been exported to Bulgaria. One loco remains UK main line registered, on spot hire to GBRf.*

| | |
|---|---|
| Built by: | BREL Crewe |
| Years introduced: | 1973-1974 |
| Wheel arrangement: | Bo-Bo |
| Weight: | 83 tons |
| Length: | 58ft 6in (17.83m) |
| Power supply: | 25kV AC |
| Control system: | HT tap changing |
| Traction output (max) | 7,680hp (5,860kW) |
| Traction output (Con): | 5,000hp (3,730kW) |
| Tractive effort: | 58,000lb |
| ETH index: | 95 |
| Maximum design speed: | 110mph (176km/h) |
| Brake Force: | 40 tons |
| Route Availability: | 6 |
| Traction Motor type: | GEC G412AZ |
| Multiple Working type: | TDM |

| | | | | | | |
|---|---|---|---|---|---|---|
| 87002 | ae | GBCH | ACL | CAL | WN | *Royal Sovereign* |

DRS Electro Diesel 88006 *Juno* passes Carlisle at the rear of a convoy of new locos from Workington Docks after delivery on 30 March 2017. *Pip Dunn*

## Class 88 Electro Diesel

*An Electro Diesel version of the Class 68 ordered for DRS. They are used mostly for intermodal trains on the West Coast Main Line. Further orders are possible.*

| | |
|---|---|
| Built by: | Vossloh/Stadler, Valencia |
| Years introduced: | 2015 |
| Wheel arrangement: | Bo-Bo |
| Weight: | 85 tons |
| Length: | 20.5m |
| Power supply: | 25kV AC |
| Engine Type: | Caterpillar C27 12-cylinder |
| Engine output: | 950hp (708kW) |
| Traction output (Con): | 5,360hp (4,000kW) |
| Tractive effort: | 71,260lbf (317kN) |
| ETH index | 96 |
| Maximum design speed: | 100mph (160km/h) |
| Brake Force: | 88 tons |
| Route Availability: | 7 |
| Main alternator type: | ABB AMXL400 |
| Traction Motor type: | ABB AMXL400 |
| Fuel tank capacity: | 400gal (1,800lit) |
| Multiple Working type: | Within Class and Class 68 only |

| | | | | | | |
|---|---|---|---|---|---|---|
| 88001 | aeup* | XHVE | BEA | DRE | CR | *Revolution* |
| 88002 | aeup* | XHVE | BEA | DRE | CR | *Prometheus* |
| 88003 | aeup* | XHVE | BEA | DRE | CR | *Genesis* |
| 88004 | aeup* | XHVE | BEA | DRE | CR | *Pandora* |
| 88005 | aeup* | XHVE | BEA | DRE | CR | *Minerva* |
| 88006 | aeup* | XHVE | BEA | DRE | CR | *Juno* |
| 88007 | aeup* | XHVE | BEA | DRE | CR | *Electra* |
| 88008 | aeup* | XHVE | BEA | DRE | CR | *Ariadne* |
| 88009 | aeup* | XHVE | BEA | DRE | CR | *Diana* |
| 88010 | aeup* | XHVE | BEA | DRE | CR | *Aurora* |

## Class 90

*An enhanced version of the Class 87 – the 90s were originally going to be Class 87/2s. 15 locos remain in passenger use with Greater Anglia but will be replaced in 2018/19. The remainder are in freight use with Freightliner and DB Cargo, but withdrawals started over a decade ago.*

| | |
|---|---|
| Built by: | BREL Crewe |
| Years introduced: | 1987-90 |
| Wheel arrangement: | Bo-Bo |
| Weight: | 84.5 tons |
| Length: | 61ft 6in (18.74m) |
| Power supply: | 25kV AC |
| Control system: | Thyristor |
| Traction output (max): | 7,680hp (5,860kW) |
| Traction output (con): | 5,000hp (3,730kW) |
| Tractive effort: | 58,000lb |
| ETH index: | 95 |
| Maximum design speed: | 110mph (176km/h) |
| Brake Force: | 40 tons |
| Route Availability: | 7 |
| Traction Motor type: | GEC G412CY |
| Multiple Working type: | TDM |

| | | | | | | | |
|---|---|---|---|---|---|---|---|
| 90001 | | aeu | IANA | POR | AGA | NC | *Crown Point* |
| 90002 | | aeu | IANA | POR | AGA | NC | *Eastern Daily Press 1870-2010 SERVING NORFOLK FOR 140 YEARS* |
| 90003 | | aeu | IANA | POR | AGA | NC | |
| 90004 | | aeu | IANA | POR | AGA | NC | *City of Chelmsford* |
| 90005 | | aeu | IANA | POR | AGA | NC | *Vice-Admiral Lord Nelson* |
| 90006 | | aeu | IANA | POR | AGA | NC | *Roger Ford/Modern Railways Magazine* |
| 90007 | | aeu | IANA | POR | AGA | NC | *Sir John Betjeman* |
| 90008 | | aeu | IANA | POR | AGA | NC | *The East Anglian* |
| 90009 | | aeu | IANA | POR | AGA | NC | |
| 90010 | | aeu | IANA | POR | AGA | NC | |
| 90011 | | aeu | IANA | POR | AGA | NC | *East Anglian Daily Times – Suffolk & Proud* |
| 90012 | | aeu | IANA | POR | AGA | NC | *Royal Anglian Regiment* |
| 90013 | | aeu | IANA | POR | AGA | NC | |
| 90014 | | aeu | IANA | POR | AGA | NC | *Norfolk & Norwich Festival* |
| 90015 | | aeu | IANA | POR | AGA | NC | *Colchester Castle* |
| 90016 | | aeu | DFLC | POR | FLR | CB | |
| 90017 | | aeu | WQBA | DBC | EWS | CE (U) | |
| 90018 | | aeu | WEAC | DBC | DBS | CE | *Pride of Bellshill* |
| 90019 | | aeu | WEDC | DBC | DBC | CE | *Multimodal* |
| 90020 | | aeu | WEDC | DBC | EWS | CE | *Collingwood* |
| 90021 | 90221 | aeu | WQAB | DBC | FSR | CE (U) | |
| 90022 | 90222 | aeu | WQBA | DBC | REW | CE (U) | *Freightconnection* |
| 90023 | 90223 | aeu | WQBA | DBC | RFE | CE (U) | |
| 90024 | 90223 | aeu | WEAC | DBC | MAA | CE | |
| 90025 | 90125, 90225 | aeu | WQBA | DBC | RFD | CE (U) | |
| 90026 | 90126 | aeu | WQAB | DBC | EWS | CE (U) | |
| 90027 | 90127, 90227 | aeu | WQBA | DBC | RFD | CE (U) | *Allerton T&RS Depot* |
| 90028 | 90128 | aeu | WEAC | DBC | EWS | CE | |
| 90029 | 90129 | aeu | WEDC | DBC | DBC | CE | |

Freightliner's 90044, still in the old grey livery, stabled at Edinburgh on 25 July 2016. *Pip Dunn*

| | | | | | | | |
|---|---|---|---|---|---|---|---|
| 90030 | 90130 | aeu | WQBA | DBC | EWS | CE (U) | |
| 90031 | 90131 | aeu | WQBA | DBC | EWS | CE (U) | *The Railway Children Partnership: Working for Street Children Worldwide* |
| 90032 | 90132 | aeu | WQBA | DBC | EWS | CE (U) | |
| 90033 | 90133, 90233 | aeu | WQBA | DBC | RFE | CE (U) | |
| 90034 | 90134 | aeu | WEDC | DBC | DRU | CE | |
| 90035 | 90135 | aeu | WEAC | DBC | EWS | CE | |
| 90036 | 90136 | aeu | WEDC | DBC | DBC | CE | *Driver Jack Mills* |
| 90037 | 90137 | aeu | WEAC | DBC | EWS | CE | *Spirit of Dagenham* |
| 90038 | 90138, 90238 | aeu | WQBA | DBC | RFE | CE (U) | |
| 90039 | 90139, 90239 | aeu | WEDC | DBC | EWS | CE | |
| 90040 | 90140 | aeu | WEAC | DBC | DBC | CE | |
| 90041 | 90141 | aeu | DFLC | POR | FLR | LD (U) | |
| 90042 | 90142 | aeu | DFLC | POR | FPH | CB | |
| 90043 | 90143 | aeu | DFLC | POR | FPH | CB | |
| 90044 | 90144 | aeu | DFLC | POR | FLG | CB | |
| 90045 | 90145 | aeu | DFLC | POR | FPH | CB | |
| 90046 | 90146 | aeu | DFLC | POR | FLR | CB | |
| 90047 | 90147 | aeu | DFLC | POR | FLG | CB | |
| 90048 | 90148 | aeu | DFLC | POR | FLG | CB | |
| 90049 | 90149 | aeu | DFLC | POR | FPH | CB | |
| 90050 | 90150 | aeu | DHLT | ARV | TTG | CB (U) | |

In its unique livery, 91110 *Battle of Britain Memorial Flight* waits at King's Cross on 28 September 2016 with the 1408 to Newark. *Pip Dunn*

## Class 91

*Dedicated express passenger locos for the East Coast Main Line, they are to be replaced by new IEP EMUs from 2018 and withdrawals or redeployment will then be inevitable. All were built as 91/0s but refurbished in 2001-03 and renumbered in the 91/1 series.*

| | |
|---|---|
| Built by: | BREL Crewe |
| Years introduced: | 1988-91 |
| Wheel arrangement: | Bo-Bo |
| Weight: | 84 tons |
| Length: | 63ft 8in (19.40m) |
| Power supply: | 25kV AC |
| Control system: | Thyristor |
| Traction output (max): | 6,300hp (4,700kW) |
| Traction output (con): | 6,090hp (4,540kW) |
| ETH index: | 95 |
| Maximum operating speed: | 125mph (200km/h) restricted to 110mph (176km/h) when flat end leading |
| Brake Force: | 45 tons |
| Route Availability: | 7 |
| Traction Motor type: | GEC G426AZ |
| Multiple Working type: | TDM |

| | | | | | | | |
|---|---|---|---|---|---|---|---|
| 91101 | 91001 | aeu | IECA | EVS | VFS | BN | *FLYING SCOTSMAN* |
| 91102 | 91002 | aeu | IECA | EVS | VEC | BN | *City of York* |
| 91103 | 91003 | aeu | IECA | EVS | VEC | BN | |
| 91104 | 91004 | aeu | IECA | EVS | VEC | BN | |
| 91105 | 91005 | aeu | IECA | EVS | VEC | BN | |
| 91106 | 91006 | aeu | IECA | EVS | VEC | BN | |
| 91107 | 91007 | aeu | IECA | EVS | VEC | BN | *SKYFALL* |
| 91108 | 91008 | aeu | IECA | EVS | VEC | BN | |

| | | | | | | | |
|---|---|---|---|---|---|---|---|
| 91109 | 91009 | aeu | IECA | EVS | VEC | BN | *Sir Bobby Robson* |
| 91110 | 91010 | aeu | IECA | EVS | BBM | BN | *BATTLE OF BRITAIN MEMORIAL FLIGHT* |
| 91111 | 91011 | aeu | IECA | EVS | FTF | BN | *For the Fallen* |
| 91112 | 91012 | aeu | IECA | EVS | VEC | BN | |
| 91113 | 91013 | aeu | IECA | EVS | VEC | BN | |
| 91114 | 91014 | aeu | IECA | EVS | VEA | BN | *Durham Cathedral* |
| 91115 | 91015 | aeu | IECA | EVS | VEC | BN | *Blaydon Races* |
| 91116 | 91016 | aeu | IECA | EVS | VEC | BN | |
| 91117 | 91017 | aeu | IECA | EVS | VEC | BN | *WEST RIDING LIMITED* |
| 91118 | 91018 | aeu | IECA | EVS | VEC | BN | |
| 91119 | 91019 | aeu | IECA | EVS | VEC | BN | *Bounds Green INTERCITY Depot 1977-2017* |
| 91120 | 91020 | aeu | IECA | EVS | VEC | BN | |
| 91121 | 91021 | aeu | IECA | EVS | VEC | BN | |
| 91122 | 91022 | aeu | IECA | EVS | VEC | BN | |
| 91124 | 91024 | aeu | IECA | EVS | VEC | BN | |
| 91125 | 91025 | aeu | IECA | EVS | VEC | BN | |
| 91126 | 91026 | aeu | IECA | EVS | VEC | BN | |
| 91127 | 91027 | aeu | IECA | EVS | VEC | BN | |
| 91128 | 91028 | aeu | IECA | EVS | VEC | BN | *INTERCITY 50* |
| 91129 | 91029 | aeu | IECA | EVS | VEC | BN | |
| 91130 | 91030 | aeu | IECA | EVS | VEC | BN | *Lord Mayor of Newcastle* |
| 91131 | 91031 | aeu | IECA | EVS | VEC | BN | |
| 91132 | 91023 | aeu | IECA | EVS | VEC | BN | |

91114 has Durham Cathedral graphics

91132 has 'time to change Employer Pledge' branding

## Class 92

*A fleet of 46 locos were ordered for Channel Tunnel work, but much of the traffic never materialised and the locos were woefully underutilised and many withdrawn from 2001.*

*Seven were owned by Eurostar, nine by SNCF and 30 by BR's Railfreight Distribution sector. The latter all transferred to EWS while GBRf has bought the other 16. Several DB Cargo locos are now in Bulgaria and Romania.*

*Two withdrawn locos are expected to be revived and overhauled for GBRf, but disposal of the remaining four is possible.*

Built by: Brush Traction
Years introduced: 1993-95
Wheel arrangement: Co-Co
Weight: 126 tons
Length: 70ft 1in (21.34m)
Power supply: 25kV AC or 750V DC
Control system: Asynchronous 3-phase
Traction output (max): 6,700hp (5,000kW) – overhead power supply
5,360hp (4,000kW) – third rail power supply
Tractive effort: Normal – 81,000lbf; boost – 90,000lbf
ETH index: 108
Maximum design speed: 87mph (139km/h)
Brake Force: 63 tons
Route Availability: 8
Traction Motor type: Brush
Multiple working type: not fitted

| | | | | | | |
|---|---|---|---|---|---|---|
| 92004 | ae | WQBA | DBC | EUE | CE (U) | *Jane Austen* |
| 92006 | ae | GBET | GBR | EUE | BL (U) | *Louis Armand* |
| 92007 | ae | WQBA | DBC | EUK | CE (U) | *Schubert* |
| 92008 | ae | WQBA | DBC | EUE | CE (U) | *Jules Verne* |
| 92009 | ae | WQBA | DBC | DBC | CE (U) | *Elgar* |
| 92010 | ae | GBST | GBR | CAL | WN | |
| 92011 | ae | WFBC | DBC | EUE | CE | *Handel* |
| 92013 | ae | WQAB | DBC | EUE | CE (U) | *Puccini* |
| 92014 | ae | GBSL | GBR | CAL | WN | |
| 92015 | ae | WFBC | DBC | DBC | CE | |
| 92016 | ae | WQAA | DBC | DBC | CE (U) | |
| 92017 | ae | WQBA | DBC | STO | CE (U) | *Bart the Engine* |
| 92018 | ae | GBST | GBR | CAL | WN | |
| 92019 | ae | WFBC | DBC | EUE | CE | *Wagner* |
| 92020 | ae | GBET | GBR | EUK | BL (U) | *Milton* |
| 92021 | ae | GBET | GBR | EUK | CO (U) | *Purcell* |
| 92023 | aed | GBST | GBR | CAL | WN | |
| 92028 | ae | GBSL | GBR | GBR | WN | |
| 92029 | ae | WQBA | DBC | EUE | CE (U) | *Dante* |
| 92031 | ae | WQAB | DBC | DBC | CE (U) | *The Institute of Logistics & Transport* |
| 92032 | ae | GBST | GBR | GBR | WN | *IMechE Railway Division* |
| 92033 | ae | GBSL | GBR | CAL | WN | |
| 92035 | ae | WQBA | DBC | EUK | CE (U) | *Mendelssohn* |
| 92036 | ae | WFBC | DBC | EUE | CE | *Bertolt Brecht* |
| 92037 | ae | WQAB | DBC | EUE | CE (U) | *Sullivan* |
| 92038 | aed | GBST | GBR | CAL | WN | |
| 92040 | ae | GBET | GBR | EUK | CO (U) | *Goethe* |
| 92041 | ae | WQAA | DBC | EUE | CE (U) | *Vaughan Williams* |
| 92042 | ae | WFBC | DBC | DBC | CE | |
| 92043 | ae | GBST | GBR | GBR | WN | |
| 92044 | ae | GBST | GBR | EUK | WN | *Couperin* |
| 92045 | ae | GBET | GBR | EUK | BL (U) | *Chaucer* |
| 92046 | ae | GBET | GBR | EUK | BL (U) | *Sweelinck* |

Note: 92009-011/015/016/018/019/023/031/032/036/038/041-043 have TVM430 in-cab signalling equipment fitted for working on HS1 lines.

The Class 92 fleet has never been used to its full potential and several locos have been withdrawn or redeployed abroad. One of the handful left in use with DB Cargo is 92042, and back on January 8 2010, it works 4S43, the 0625 Rugby-Mossend, past Hairdrigg, between Oxenholme and Tebay. This loco is now in DB Red. *Anthony Hicks*

# 2 Spot hire and industrial locos

This section lists all locos regarded as available for short term or medium term spot hire but do not have full main line registration, plus locos that have been sold or moved abroad on a long term basis. Not all locos are necessarily in operation and some may have been disposed of.

| Loco's current TOPS number | Previous official numbers carried | Key detail differences | Current TOPS Sector | Vehicle Owner | Current Livery | Current depot allocation or location | Current name (as displayed on the loco) Minor wording on crests, plaques or graphics is excluded |
|---|---|---|---|---|---|---|---|

## Class 03

| | | | | | | | |
|---|---|---|---|---|---|---|---|
| 03084 | D2084 | xow | | CRB | GWS | CS | |
| 03196 | D2196 | xow | | WCR | BRW | CS (U) | |
| | D2381 | vo | | WCR | GNY | CS (U) | |

## Class 07

| | | | | | | | |
|---|---|---|---|---|---|---|---|
| 07007 | D2991 | vo | | AFS | BRW | ZG | |
| 07011 | D2995 | xow | | SLE | BRW | SE | |

## Class 08

| | | | | | | | |
|---|---|---|---|---|---|---|---|
| 08021 | D3029, 13029 | vo | | TLW | BLK | TM | |
| 08168 | D3236, 13236 | vo | | NEM | BLK | EOR | |
| 08220 | D3290, 13290 | vo | | EEG | BRW | ZW | |
| 08296 | D3955, 08787 | xo | | AGI | BLE | MQ (U) | |
| 08308 | D3378 | ao | MRSO | RMS | FSR | PD | |
| 08375 | D3460 | ao | MRSO | RMS | BLK | SS | |
| 08389 | D3504 | ao | HNRS | HNR | EWS | CC | |
| 08401 | D3516 | ao | | HUN | HUN | HH | |
| 08405 | D3520 | ao | MBDL | DBC | EWS | NL | |
| 08423 | D3538 | ao | | RMS | RMS | PD | |
| 08428 | D3543 | ao | HNRL | HNR | EWS | BH (U) | |
| 08441 | D3556 | ao | MBDL | RSS | RSS | BN | |
| 08442 | D3557 | ao | | ARV | LNW | EH (U) | |
| 08445 | D3560 | ao | | HUN | MAL | DD | |
| 08447 | D3562 | ao | | DST | DST | DS | |
| 08460 | D3575 | ao | MBDL | RSS | RSS | LP | *SPIRIT OF THE OAK* |
| 08484 | D3599 | ao | MBDL | RSS | RSS | WC | *CAPTAIN NATHANIEL DARELL* |
| 08499 | D3654 | ao | | PUL | BLE | CF | *REDLIGHT* |
| 08500 | D3655 | ao | HNRL | HNR | EWS | BU (U) | |
| 08502 | D3657 | ao | HNRL | HNR | NOR | BH | |
| 08503 | D3658 | ao | HNRL | HNC | BLU | BIR | |
| 08516 | D3678 | ao | | ARV | LNW | BK | *RORY* |
| 08527 | D3689 | ao | HNRL | HNR | TTG | PU | |
| 08536 | D3700 | xo | HISE | LOR | BRW | DF (U) | |
| 08567 | D3734 | ao | MBDL | AFS | EWS | ZG | |
| 08568 | D3735 | xo | MBDL | KBR | RCG | ZH | *St Rollox* |
| 08573 | D3740 | xo | MRSO | RMS | BLK | ZI | |
| 08578 | D3745 | ao | HNRS | HNR | EWS | LM (U) | |
| 08580 | D3747 | xo | MBDL | RSS | EWS | WI (U) | |
| 08593 | D3760 | ao | MBDL | RSS | EWS | WI (U) | |
| 08600 | D3767, 97800 | ao | | AVD | AVD | MB | |
| 08602 | D3769 | ao | | BOM | BLE | ZD | |
| 08605 | D3772 | ao | RTSO | RIV | DBS | SP | |
| 08613 | D3780 | ao | | RMS | RMS | WO | |

| | | | | | | | |
|---|---|---|---|---|---|---|---|
| 08615 | D3782 | ao | RFSH | WAB | BLK | LH | |
| 08622 | D3789 | ao | | RMS | BLK | WO | |
| 08623 | D3790 | ao | | HNR | DBS | HO (U) | |
| 08629 | D3796 | xo | RCZN | KBR | KBR | ZN | *Wolverton* |
| 08630 | D3797 | ao | HNRL | HNR | CEL | CC | *Celsa Endeavour* |
| 08632 | D3799 | ao | MBDL | RSS | RSS | TR | |
| 08643 | D3810 | xo | MBDL | AGI | GRE | MD | |
| 08648 | D3815 | ao | MRSO | RMS | GCR | HT | |
| 08649 | D3816 | xo | RCZN | KBR | KBR | ZN | *Bradwell* |
| 08650 | D3817 | xow | | AGI | BRY | ZG | *ISLE OF GRAIN* |
| 08652 | D3819 | ao | | AGI | BRY | MD | |
| 08653 | D3820 | xo | HNRS | HNR | EWS | LM (U) | |
| 08669 | D3836 | ao | RFSH | WAB | BLK | ZB | *Bob Machin* |
| 08676 | D3843 | xo | HNRL | HNR | EWS | EKR | |
| 08682 | D3849 | xo | KDSD | BOM | SPE | ZD | *Lionheart* |
| 08685 | D3852 | ao | HNRS | HNR | EWS | EKR | |
| 08699 | D3866 | xo | MBDL | RMS | BLE | WO (U) | |
| 08700 | D3867 | xo | | HNR | BRW | ZI | |
| 08701 | D3868 | xo | HNRS | HNR | RES | LM (U) | |
| 08703 | D3870 | ao | MBDL | RSS | EWS | SP | |
| 08706 | D3873 | ao | | HNR | EWS | WI (U) | |
| 08709 | D3876 | xo | MBDL | RSS | EWS | WI (U) | |
| 08711 | D3878 | ao | HNRS | HNR | RES | BU (U) | |
| 08714 | D3881 | ao | MBDL | HNR | EWS | HO (U) | |
| 08724 | D3892 | xo | HBSH | WAB | BLK | ZB | |
| 08730 | D3898 | xo | RCZH | KBR | KBR | ZH | |
| 08738 | D3906 | ao | MBDL | RSS | ECR | WI (U) | |
| 08742 | D3910 | ao | HNRL | HNR | RES | DRC | |
| 08743 | D3911 | ao | MBDL | ICI | BLE | BB | *Bryan Turner* |
| 08750 | D3918 | xo | MRSO | RMS | BLK | WO (U) | |
| 08752 | D3920 | ao | MBDL | RSS | EWS | WI (U) | |
| 08754 | D3922 | ao | RMSX | RMS | RMS | NC | |
| 08756 | D3924 | ao | MRSO | RMS | DEP | SS | |
| 08762 | D3930 | ao | MRSO | RMS | BLK | DF | |
| 08764 | D3932 | aod | | RMS | BRW | PO | |
| 08765 | D3933 | ao | HNRS | HNR | HNO | BH (U) | |
| 08774 | D3942 | ao | | AVD | AVD | MB | *ARTHUR VERNON DAWSON* |
| 08782 | D3950 | ao | HNRL | HNR | COR | BH (U) | |
| 08783 | D3951 | ao | | EMR | EWS | ZO (U) | |
| 08786 | D3954 | ao | HNRS | HNR | DEP | BH (U) | |
| 08788 | D3956 | ao | MRSO | RMS | RMS | WO | |
| 08798 | D3966 | ao | | EMR | EWS | AT (U) | |
| 08799 | D3967 | ao | | HNR | EWS | EK | |
| 08802 | D3971 | ao | HNRS | HNR | EWS | WI (U) | |
| 08804 | D3972 | ao | | HNR | EWS | EK | |
| 08809 | D3977 | xo | MRSO | RMS | RMS | PD | |
| 08810 | D3978 | ao | MBDL | ARV | LNW | CP | *RICHARD J. WENHAM EASTLEIGH DEPOT* |
| 08818 | D3986 | ao | HNRL | HNR | GBR | FG | *MOLLY* |
| 08823 | D3991 | ao | KDSD | HUN | MAL | DD | *LIBBIE* |
| 08824 | D3992 | ao | HNRL | HNR | BLK | BH (U) | |
| 08834 | D4002 | xo | HNRL | HNR | HNR | AN | |
| 08846 | D4014 | xo | | BOM | BLE | WI (U) | |
| 08847 | D4015 | xow | MBDL | RMS | COT | NC | |
| 08853 | D4021 | ao | RFSH | WAB | BLK | ZB | |
| 08865 | D4033 | ao | HNRL | HNR | EWS | HO (U) | |
| 08868 | D4036 | xo | MBDL | ARV | LNW | CP | |

| | | | | | | | |
|---|---|---|---|---|---|---|---|
| 08870 | D4038 | xo | MBDL | RMS | CAS | KT | |
| 08871 | D4039 | xo | MBDL | RMS | COT | TR | |
| 08872 | D4040 | xo | | EMR | EWS | AT | |
| 08873 | D4041 | ao | DFLS | HUN | RES | SM | |
| 08874 | D4042 | xo | MBDL | RMS | SIL | SS | |
| 08877 | D4045 | xo | HNRS | HNR | DEP | BH | *WIGAN 1* |
| 08879 | D4047 | xo | WQAA | AFS | EWS | ZG | |
| 08885 | D4115 | xo | | RMS | RMS | WO (U) | |
| 08892 | D4122 | xo | HNRL | HNR | DRS | AH | |
| 08903 | D4133 | ao | MBDL | ICI | BLE | BB | *John W Antill* |
| 08904 | D4134 | ao | HNRL | HNR | EWS | CC | |
| 08905 | D4135 | ao | HNRS | HNR | EWS | HO (U) | |
| 08912 | D4142 | ao | | AVD | BRW | MB (U) | |
| 08913 | D4143 | ao | | RMS | MAL | LH | |
| 08918 | D4148 | xo | HNRS | HNR | DEP | BU (U) | |
| 08921 | D4151 | ao | | EMR | EWS | ZO (U) | |
| 08924 | D4154 | ao | HNRS | HNR | GBR | CC | |
| 08927 | D4157 | xo | MBDL | AGO | GWS | RR | |
| 08933 | D4163 | aow | | AGI | BRY | MD | |
| 08936 | D4166 | ao | MBDL | RMS | RMS | SS | |
| 08939 | D4169 | ao | MBDL | RSS | ECR | WI (U) | |
| 08943 | D4173 | xo | HNRL | HNR | HNR | CZ | |
| 08944 | D4174 | xo | | HNR | BLK | BQ (U) | |
| 08947 | D4177 | ao | | AGI | BRY | MD | |
| 08954 | D4184 | ao | HNRL | HNR | BRW | PO | |
| 08956 | D4186 | xo | CDJD | SEC | BRW | WI | |
| 08994 | D3577, 08462 | ao | HNRS | HNR | EWS | BU (U) | |

08738/939 are fitted with nose end scaffolding and AAR multiple working

08428/511/578/588/630/652/685/703/706/711/737/762/824/905/924/947 have swinghead couplers

## Class 09

| | | | | | | |
|---|---|---|---|---|---|---|
| 09006 | D3670 | xo | HNRS | HNR | EWS | BU (U) |
| 09014 | D4102 | xo | HNRS | HNR | DEP | BU (U) |
| 09022 | D4110 | ao | | VIC | BDB | BD |
| 09023 | D4111 | ao | | EMR | EWS | AT (U) |
| 09106 | D3927, 08759 | ao | HNRL | HNR | DBS | DG |
| 09201 | D3536, 08421 | ao | HNRL | HNR | DEP | HO (U) |
| 09204 | D3884, 08717 | ao | MBDL | ARV | ARV | CP |

09023/106/201 have swinghead couplers

## Class 20

| | | | | | | | |
|---|---|---|---|---|---|---|---|
| 20016 | D8016 | xo | HNRS | HNR | BRB | LM (U) | |
| 20056 | D8056 | ao | HNRL | HNR | COY | SC (U) | |
| 20066 | D8066 | ao | | HNR | TAT | HO (U) | |
| 20069 | D8069 | xo | | HNR | BRB | TX (U) | |
| 20081 | D8081 | xop | HNRS | HNR | BRB | LM (U) | |
| 20087 | D8087 | xop | MBDL | HNR | BRB | BQ (U) | |
| 20088 | D8088 | xop | HNRS | HNR | RFS | LM (U) | |
| 20110 | D8110 | xop | | HNR | GYP | BQ (S) | |
| 20121 | D8121 | aop | HNRS | HNR | HNO | BH (U) | |
| 20166 | D8166 | aop | HNRL | HNR | HNO | WR | |
| 20168 | D8168, 20304 | aop | HNRL | HNR | HOP | HO | *SIR GEORGE EARLE* |
| 20903 | D8083, 20083 | aotp | HNRS | HNR | DRU | BU (U) | |
| 20904 | D8041, 20041 | aotp | HNRS | HNR | DRU | BU (U) | |
| 20906 | D8319, 20219 | aotp | HNRL | HNR | HOP | HO | |

One of the RMS Locotec fleet, 08613 stand at the exchange sidings at Ketton Cement Works on 3 November 2010. This loco is now at Wolsingham. *Pip Dunn*

HNRC owns several Class 20s, some of which are on hire to main line operators and others which have been in industrial use. 20056 was based at the steelworks at Scunthorpe and is seen on 19 April 2014. The loco remains at the site but is no longer on hire and is in need of major repairs. *Pip Dunn*

25278 has partial main line registration but is limited to the Middlesbrough-Whitby branch. On 27 June 2015 it pauses at Glaisdale with the 1214 Battersby-Grosmont. *Pip Dunn*

## Class 25

| | | | | | | | |
|---|---|---|---|---|---|---|---|
| 25278 | D7628 | xo | MBDL | NYM | GYP | GO | *SYBILLA* |

## Class 31

| | | | | | | | |
|---|---|---|---|---|---|---|---|
| 31106 | D5524 | xo | RVLO | HJE | BRB | WO (U) | |
| 31128 | D5546 | xop | NRLO | NEM | BRB | BU (S) | *Charybdis* |
| 31235 | D5662 | xo | | HNR | BRB | TX (U) | |
| 31255 | D5683 | xo | MBDL | HNR | EWS | CV (U) | |
| 31285 | D5817 | ao | HNRL | HNR | NRY | WO | |
| 31459 | D5684, 31256 | xe | RVLO | HNR | BRN | WO | |
| 31461 | D5547, 31129 | xe | NRLO | NEM | CCE | WO | |
| 31465 | D5637, 31213, 31565 | aep | HNRL | HNR | NRY | WO | |

31285 has additional spotlights and recording cameras fitted at No. 2 end

## Class 37

| | | | | | | |
|---|---|---|---|---|---|---|
| 37198 | D6898 | xotp | MBDL | NET | NRY | BU (U) |
| 37255 | D6955 | xotp | NRLS | NEM | CCE | BU (U) |
| 37503 | D6717, 37017 | aotp | EPUK | EPX | EWS | LR (U) |
| 37510 | D6812, 37112 | aotp | EPUK | EPX | DRC | LR (U) |
| 37612 | D6879, 37179, 37691 | aotpr | XHSS | HNR | DRC | BH (U) |
| 37670 | D6882, 37182 | aotp | EPUK | EPX | DBS | LR (U) |

Nemesis Rail has just one loco which has been main line registered of late, but 31128 *Charybdis* is currently at Burton available for hire. On 16 September 2012 the loco stands at Grosmont while on hire to the NYMR. *Pip Dunn*

37608 is owned by Europhoenix for spot hire and has been mostly used by Colas Rail Freight. With DRS's 37604 on the rear, the immaculate loco works 1Q05, the 0612 Derby-Tees Yard test train past Freemans Crossing near Ashington on 23 January 2017. *Anthony Hicks*

## Class 47

| | | | | | | | |
|---|---|---|---|---|---|---|---|
| 47488 | D1713 | xet | NRLS | NEM | GYP | BU (U) | *Waverley* |
| 47701 | D1932, 47493 | xet | NRLO | NEM | TWO | BU (U) | |
| 47703 | D1960, 47514 | xet | HNRS | HNR | UND | ZF (U) | |
| 47714 | D1955, 47511 | xet | HNRL | HNR | ANG | AH | |
| 47715 | D1945, 47502 | xet | HNRL | HNR | NSD | WR | *Haymarket* |
| 47744 | D1927, 47250, 47600 | xet | NRLS | NEM | EWS | BU (U) | |
| 47769 | D1753, 47491 | xetm | HNRS | HNR | VIR | BH (U) | *Resolve* |
| 47810 | D1924, 47247, 47655 | aetm | MBDL | AFS | DRU | ZG (U) | |
| 47818 | D1917, 47240, 47663 | aetm | MBDL | AFS | DRU | ZG (U) | |
| 47853 | D1733, 47141, 47614 | aetm | GBHN | HNR | DRU | BH (U) | |

## Class 56

| | | | | | | |
|---|---|---|---|---|---|---|
| 56007 | | aos | UKRS | UKR | FER | LR (U) |
| 56009 | | aos | UKRS | UKR | BLE | BL (U) |
| 56018 | | aos | UKRS | UKR | FER | LR (U) |
| 56031 | | aos | UKRS | UKR | FER | LR (U) |
| 56032 | | aos | UKRS | UKR | FER | LR (U) |
| 56037 | | aos | UKRS | UKR | EWS | LR (U) |
| 56038 | | aos | UKRS | UKR | FER | LR (U) |
| 56060 | | aos | UKRS | UKR | FER | LR (U) |
| 56065 | | aos | UKRS | UKR | FER | LR (U) |
| 56069 | | aos | UKRS | UKR | FER | LR (U) |
| 56077 | | aos | UKRS | UKR | LHO | LR (U) |
| 56106 | | aos | UKRS | UKR | FER | LR (U) |

## Class 66

| | | | | | | |
|---|---|---|---|---|---|---|
| 66048 | | aost | | EMD | UND | ZW (U) |

## Class 73

| | | | | | | | |
|---|---|---|---|---|---|---|---|
| 73101 | E6007, 73801 | xew | | LOR | PUL | DF (U) | *The Royal Alex'* |
| 73133 | E6040 | xew | MBED | TMT | TMT | ZG | |
| 73139 | E6046 | xew | MRLS | LOR | LOR | DF (U) | |

## Class 86

| | | | | | | |
|---|---|---|---|---|---|---|
| 86229 | E3119 | ae | EPEX | FLI | VIR | LM (U) |
| 86251 | E3101 | ae | EPEX | FLI | VIR | LM (U) |
| 86901 | E3136, 86044, 86253 | ae | QACL | FLI | NRY | CB (U) |

To date the only Class 47 export is 47375 *Falcon* which is now used by Continental Rail Solutions in Hungary. It stands at Bakonysárkány in the north west of the country with a charter train on 24 May 2017. *Mark Hare*

# Exported locos

| Loco's current number | Previous UK numbers | Key detail difference | Current TOPS Sector | Vehicle Owner | Current Livery | Current depot allocation or location | Current name |
|---|---|---|---|---|---|---|---|
| **Class 04** | | | | | | | |
| | D2289 | vo | | ITY | RED | | |
| **Class 08** | | | | | | | |
| D3047 | 13047 | vo | | LAM | LAM | | |
| D3092 | 13092 | vo | | LAM | LAM | | |
| Note: Both these locos may have been scrapped. | | | | | | | |
| **Class 47** | | | | | | | |
| 92 70 00 47375-5 | 47375, D1894 | aot | NRLO | CON | CSM | HUN | *FALCON* |
| **Class 56** | | | | | | | |
| 92 55 0659 001-5 | 56101 | ao | | FLY | FLY | HUN | |
| 92 55 0659 002-3 | 56115 | ao | | FLY | FLY | HUN | |
| 92 55 0659 003-1 | 56117 | ao | | FLY | FER | HUN (U) | |

## Class 58

| | | | | | | | |
|---|---|---|---|---|---|---|---|
| | 58001 | aosp | WQCA | DBC | ETF | AZ (U) | |
| | 58004 | aosp | WQCA | DBC | TSO | AZ (U) | |
| | 58005 | aosp | WQCA | DBC | ETF | AZ (U) | |
| | 58006 | aosp | WQCA | DBC | ETF | AZ (U) | |
| | 58007 | aosp | WQCA | DBC | TSO | AZ (U) | |
| | 58009 | aosp | WQCA | DBC | TSO | AZ (U) | |
| | 58010 | aosp | WQCA | DBC | TSO | AZ (U) | |
| | 58011 | aosp | WQCA | DBC | TSO | AZ (U) | |
| | 58013 | aosp | WQCA | DBC | ETF | AZ (U) | |
| L54 | 58015 | aosp | | TFA | CON | AC | |
| | 58018 | aosp | WQCA | DBC | TSO | AZ (U) | |
| L43 | 58020 | aosp | | TFA | CON | AC | |
| | 58021 | aosp | WQCA | DBC | ETF | AZ (U) | |
| L42 | 58024 | aosp | | TFA | CON | AC | |
| | 58025 | aosp | WQCA | DBC | CON | AB (U) | |
| | 58026 | aosp | WQCA | DBC | TSO | AZ (U) | |
| L52 | 58027 | aosp | WQCA | DBC | CON | AB (U) | |
| L44 | 58029 | aosp | | TFA | CON | AC (U) | |
| L46 | 58030 | aosp | | TFA | CON | AC | |
| L45 | 58031 | aosp | | TFA | CON | AC | *Caballero Ferroviario* |
| | 58032 | aosp | WQCA | DBC | ETF | AZ (U) | |
| | 58033 | aosp | WQCA | DBC | TSO | AZ (U) | |
| | 58034 | aosp | WQCA | DBC | TSO | AZ (U) | |
| | 58035 | aosp | WQCA | DBC | TSO | AZ (U) | |
| | 58036 | aosp | WQCA | DBC | ETF | AZ (U) | |
| | 58038 | aosp | | TFA | ETF | AZ (U) | |
| | 58039 | aosp | WQCA | DBC | ETF | AZ (U) | |
| | 58040 | aosp | WQCA | DBC | TSO | AZ (U) | |
| L36 | 58041 | aosp | | TFA | CON | AB (U) | |
| | 58042 | aosp | WQCA | DBC | ETF | AZ (U) | |
| L37 | 58043 | aosp | | TFA | CON | AC | |
| | 58044 | aosp | WQCA | DBC | ETF | WP (U) | |
| | 58046 | aosp | WQCA | DBC | TSO | AZ (U) | |
| L51 | 58047 | aosp | | TFA | CON | AC | |
| | 58049 | aosp | WQCA | DBC | ETF | AZ (U) | |
| L53 | 58050 | aosp | WQCA | DBC | CON | AB (U) | |

## Class 66

| | | | | | | |
|---|---|---|---|---|---|---|
| 92 70 0 066010-4 | 66010 | aos | WGEA | DBC | EWS | AZ |
| 92 70 0 066022-9 | 66022 | aos | WGEA | DBC | EWS | AZ |
| 92 70 0 066026-0 | 66026 | aos | WGEA | DBC | EWS | AZ |
| 92 70 0 066028-6 | 66028 | aos | WGEA | DBC | EWS | AZ |
| 92 70 0 066029-4 | 66029 | aos | WGEA | DBC | EWS | AZ |
| 92 70 0 066032-8 | 66032 | aos | WGEA | DBC | EWS | AZ |
| 92 70 0 066033-6 | 66033 | aos | WGEA | DBC | EWS | AZ |
| 92 70 0 066036-9 | 66036 | aos | WGEA | DBC | EWS | AZ |
| 92 70 0 066038-5 | 66038 | aos | WGEA | DBC | EWS | AZ |
| 92 70 0 066042-7 | 66042 | aos | WGEA | DBC | EWS | AZ |
| 92 70 0 066045-0 | 66045 | aos | WGEA | DBC | EWS | AZ |
| 92 70 0 066049-2 | 66049 | aos | WGEA | DBC | EWS | AZ |
| 92 70 0 066052-6 | 66052 | aos | WGEA | DBC | EWS | AZ |
| 92 70 0 066062-5 | 66062 | aos | WGEA | DBC | EWS | AZ |
| 92 70 0 066064-1 | 66064 | aos | WGEA | DBC | EWS | AZ |

| | | | | | | |
|---|---|---|---|---|---|---|
| 92 70 0 066071-6 | 66071 | aos | WGEA | DBC | EWS | AZ |
| 92 70 0 066072-4 | 66072 | aos | WGEA | DBC | EWS | AZ |
| 92 70 0 066073-2 | 66073 | aos | WGEA | DBC | EWS | AZ |
| 92 70 0 066123-5 | 66123 | aos | WGEA | DBC | EWS | AZ |
| 92 70 0 066146-6 | 66146 | aos | WGEP | DBC | EWS | PN |
| 92 70 0 066153-2 | 66153 | aos | WGEP | DBC | EWS | PN |
| 92 70 0 066157-3 | 66157 | aos | WGEP | DBC | EWS | PN |
| 92 70 0 066159-9 | 66159 | aos | WGEP | DBC | EWS | PN |
| 92 70 0 066163-1 | 66163 | aos | WGEP | DBC | DBR | PN |
| 92 70 0 066166-4 | 66166 | aos | WGEP | DBC | EWS | PN |
| 92 70 0 066173-0 | 66173 | aos | WGEP | DBC | EWS | PN |
| 92 70 0 066178-9 | 66178 | aos | WGEP | DBC | DBR | PN |
| 92 70 0 066179-7 | 66179 | aos | WGEA | DBC | EWS | AZ |
| 92 70 0 066180-5 | 66180 | aos | WGEP | DBC | EWS | PN |
| 92 70 0 066189-6 | 66189 | aos | WGEP | DBC | DBR | PN |
| 92 70 0 066190-4 | 66190 | aos | WGEA | DBC | EWS | AZ |
| 92 70 0 066191-2 | 66191 | aos | WGEA | DBC | EWS | AZ |
| 92 70 0 066193-8 | 66193 | aos | WGEA | DBC | EWS | AZ |
| 92 70 0 066195-3 | 66195 | aos | WGEA | DBC | EWS | AZ |
| 92 70 0 066196-1 | 66196 | aos | WGEP | DBC | EWS | PN |
| 92 70 0 066201-9 | 66201 | aos | WGEA | DBC | EWS | AZ |
| 92 70 0 066202-7 | 66202 | aos | WGEA | DBC | EWS | AZ |
| 92 70 0 066203-5 | 66203 | aos | WGEA | DBC | EWS | AZ |
| 92 70 0 066204-3 | 66204 | aos | WGEA | DBC | EWS | AZ |
| 92 70 0 066205-1 | 66205 | aos | WGEA | DBC | EWS | AZ |
| 92 70 0 066208-4 | 66208 | aos | WGEA | DBC | EWS | AZ |
| 92 70 0 066209-2 | 66209 | aos | WGEA | DBC | EWS | AZ |
| 92 70 0 066210-0 | 66210 | aos | WGEA | DBC | EWS | AZ |
| 92 70 0 066211-8 | 66211 | aos | WGEA | DBC | EWS | AZ |
| 92 70 0 066212-6 | 66212 | aos | WGEA | DBC | EWS | AZ |
| 92 70 0 066213-4 | 66213 | aos | WGEA | DBC | EWS | AZ |
| 92 70 0 066214-2 | 66214 | aos | WGEA | DBC | EWS | AZ |
| 92 70 0 066215-9 | 66215 | aos | WGEA | DBC | EWS | AZ |
| 92 70 0 066216-7 | 66216 | aos | WGEA | DBC | EWS | AZ |
| 92 70 0 066217-5 | 66217 | aos | WGEA | DBC | EWS | AZ |
| 92 70 0 066218-3 | 66218 | aos | WGEA | DBC | EWS | AZ |
| 92 70 0 066219-1 | 66219 | aos | WGEA | DBC | EWS | AZ |
| 92 70 0 066220-9 | 66220 | aos | WGEP | DBC | DBR | PN |
| 92 70 0 066222-5 | 66222 | aos | WGEA | DBC | EWS | AZ |
| 92 70 0 066223-3 | 66223 | aos | WGEA | DBC | EWS | AZ |
| 92 70 0 066224-1 | 66224 | aos | WGEA | DBC | EWS | AZ |
| 92 70 0 066225-8 | 66225 | aos | WGEA | DBC | EWS | AZ |
| 92 70 0 066226-6 | 66226 | aos | WGEA | DBC | EWS | AZ |
| 92 70 0 066227-4 | 66227 | aos | WGEP | DBC | DBR | PN |
| 92 70 0 066228-2 | 66228 | aos | WGEA | DBC | EWS | AZ |
| 92 70 0 066229-0 | 66229 | aos | WGEA | DBC | EWS | AZ |
| 92 70 0 066231-6 | 66231 | aos | WGEA | DBC | EWS | AZ |
| 92 70 0 066232-4 | 66232 | aos | WGEA | DBC | EWS | AZ |
| 92 70 0 066233-2 | 66233 | aos | WGEA | DBC | EWS | AZ |
| 92 70 0 066234-0 | 66234 | aos | WGEA | DBC | EWS | AZ |
| 92 70 0 066235-7 | 66235 | aos | WGEA | DBC | EWS | AZ |
| 92 70 0 066236-5 | 66236 | aos | WGEA | DBC | EWS | AZ |
| 92 70 0 066237-3 | 66237 | aos | WGEP | DBC | EWS | PN |
| 92 70 0 066239-9 | 66239 | aos | WGEA | DBC | EWS | AZ |
| 92 70 0 066240-7 | 66240 | aos | WGEA | DBC | EWS | AZ |
| 92 70 0 066241-5 | 66241 | aos | WGEA | DBC | EWS | AZ |

Several DB Cargo Class 66s have been redeployed to work in France or Poland. The French locos, used by Euro Cargo Rail, occasionally return to the UK for heavy maintenance. On January 16 2015, one of the ECR locos, 66242, was back at Toton alongside 66167. *Anthony Hicks*

| | | | | | | |
|---|---|---|---|---|---|---|
| 92 70 0 066242-3 | 66242 | aos | WGEA | DBC | EWS | AZ |
| 92 70 0 066243-1 | 66243 | aos | WGEA | DBC | EWS | AZ |
| 92 70 0 066244-9 | 66244 | aos | WGEA | DBC | EWS | AZ |
| 92 70 0 066245-6 | 66245 | aos | WGEA | DBC | EWS | AZ |
| 92 70 0 066246-4 | 66246 | aos | WGEA | DBC | EWS | AZ |
| 92 70 0 066247-2 | 66247 | aos | WGEA | DBC | EWS | AZ |
| 92 70 0 066248-9 | 66248 | aos | WGEP | DBC | DBR | PN |
| 92 70 0 066249-8 | 66249 | aos | WGEA | DBC | EWS | AZ |
| 66013 | 66411 | aos | DHLT | MAQ | FPH | FP |
| 66015 | 66412 | aos | DHLT | MAQ | FPH | FP |
| 66014 | 66417 | aos | DHLT | MAQ | FPH | FP |
| 66016 | 66527 | aos | DHLT | EVS | FLR | FP |
| 66017 | 66530 | aos | DHLT | POR | FLR | FP |
| 66018 | 66535 | aos | DHLT | POR | FLR | FP |
| 66009 | 66582 | aos | DHLT | EVS | FLR | FP |
| 66010 | 66583 | aos | DHLT | EVS | FLR | FP |
| 66011 | 66584 | aos | DHLT | EVS | FLR | FP |
| 66008 | 66586 | aos | DHLT | MAQ | FLR | FP |
| 66603 | 66608 | aos | DHLT | POR | FLR | FP |
| 66605 | 66609 | aos | DHLT | POR | FLR | FP |
| 66604 | 66611 | aos | DHLT | POR | FLR | FP |
| 66606 | 66612 | aos | DHLT | POR | FLR | FP |
| 66602 | 66624 | aos | DHLT | MAQ | FLR | FP |
| 66601 | 66625 | aos | DHLT | MAQ | FLR | FP |

Note: The Freightliner Poland locos have been renumbered in the 660xx series for Class 66/5s and 6660x series for Class 66/6s. FPL also owns seven 'Class 66s' numbered 66001-007 which were new-build locos and did not work in the UK.

DB Cargo's Euro Cargo Rail subsidiary also operates 60 'Class 66s', numbered 77001-060 which were new-build locos and did not work in the UK.

All WGEP locos have their swinghead couplers removed. WGEA locos retain them.

## Class 86

| | | | | | | |
|---|---|---|---|---|---|---|
| 91 52 00 87703-2 | 86213, E3193 | ae | BMT | BMT | BUL | *Lancashire Witch* |
| 91 55 0450 005-6 | 86215, E3165 | ae | FLY | FLY | HUN | |
| 91 55 0450 006-6 | 86217, E3177 | ae | FLY | FLY | HUN | |
| 91 55 0450 004-1 | 86218, E3175 | ae | FLY | FLY | HUN | |
| 91 55 0450 007-4 | 86228, E3167 | ae | FLY | FLY | HUN | |
| | 86231, E3126 | ae | BMT | BMT | BUL | *Lady of the Lake* |
| 91 55 0450 003-3 | 86232, E3113 | ae | FLY | FLY | HUN | |
| | 86233, E3172 | ae | BMT | EBY | BUL (U) | |
| 9152 00 85005-2 | 86234, E3155 | ae | BMT | BMT | BUL | |
| 9152 00 85004-7 | 86235, E3194 | ae | BMT | BMT | BUL | *Novelty* |
| 91 55 0450 008-2 | 86242, E3138 | ae | FLY | FLY | HUN | |
| 91 55 0450 001-7 | 86248, E3107 | ae | FLY | FLY | HUN | |
| 91 55 0450 002-5 | 86250, E3189 | ae | FLY | FLY | HUN | |
| 91 55 0450 009-0 | 86424, E3111, 86024, 86324 | ae | FLY | NRY | HUN (U) | |
| 91 52 00 87701-6 | 86701, E3128, 86205, 86503 | ae | BMT | BMT | BUL | *Orion* |
| 91 52 00 87702-4 | 86702 E3144, 86048, 86260 | ae | BMT | BMT | BUL | *Cassiopeia* |

## Class 87

| | | | | | | |
|---|---|---|---|---|---|---|
| 91 52 00 87003-7 | 87003 | ae | BZK | BZK | BUL | |
| 91 52 00 87004-5 | 87004 | ae | BZK | BRZ | BUL | *Britannia* |
| 91 52 00 87006-0 | 87006 | ae | BZK | DGB | BUL (U) | |
| 91 52 00 87007-8 | 87007 | ae | BZK | COT | BUL | |
| 91 52 00 87008-9 | 87008 | ae | BZK | COT | BUL (U) | |
| 91 52 00 87009-4 | 87009 | ae | BMT | BMT | BUL | |
| 91 52 00 87010-2 | 87010 | ae | BZK | BZK | BUL | |
| 91 52 00 87012-8 | 87012 | ae | BZK | NSE | BUL | |
| 91 52 00 87013-6 | 87013 | ae | BZK | BZK | BUL | |
| 91 52 00 87014-7 | 87014 | ae | BZK | BZK | BUL (U) | |
| 91 52 00 87017-7 | 87017 | ae | BMT | EPX | BUL | *Iron Duke* |
| 91 52 00 87019-3 | 87019 | ae | BZK | LNR | BUL | |
| 91 52 00 87020-1 | 87020 | ae | BZK | BZK | BUL | |
| 91 52 00 87022-7 | 87022 | ae | BZK | DGB | BUL | |
| 91 52 00 87023-5 | 87023 | ae | BMT | EPX | BUL | *Velocity* |
| 91 52 00 87025-0 | 87025 | ae | BMT | BMT | BUL | |
| 91 52 00 87026-8 | 87026 | ae | BZK | BZK | BUL | |
| 91 52 00 87028-4 | 87028 | ae | BZK | DRS | BUL | |
| 91 52 00 87029-2 | 87029 | ae | BZK | BZK | BUL | |
| 91 52 00 87033-4 | 87033 | ae | BZK | BZK | BUL | |
| 91 52 00 87034-2 | 87034 | ae | BZK | BZK | BUL (U) | |

## Class 92

| | | | | | | | |
|---|---|---|---|---|---|---|---|
| 91 53 0 472 002-1 | 92001 | ae | WGEE | DBC | DBR | DC | *Mircea Elaide* |
| 91 53 0 472 003-9 | 92002 | ae | WGEE | DBC | DBR | DC | *Lucian Blaga* |
| | 92003 | ae | WGEE | DBC | EUE | DK | *Beethoven* |
| 91 53 0 472 005-4 | 92005 | ae | WGEE | DBC | DBR | DK | *Emil Cioran* |
| 91 53 0 472 001-3 | 92012 | ae | WGEE | DBC | DBR | DC | *Mihai Eminescu* |
| | 92022 | ae | WGEE | DBC | EUE | DM (U) | *Charles Dickens* |
| 91 53 0 472 004-7 | 92024 | ae | WGEE | DBC | DBR | DC | *Marin Preda* |
| 91 70 00 92025-1 | 92025 | ae | WGEE | DBC | EUE | DK | *Oscar Wilde* |
| | 92026 | ae | WGEE | DBC | EUE | DK | *Britten* |
| 91 70 00 92027-7 | 92027 | ae | WGEE | DBC | EUE | DK | *George Eliot* |
| 91 52 16 88030-1 | 92030 | ae | WGEE | DBC | EUE | DK | *Ashford* |
| 91 70 00 92034-3 | 92034 | ae | WGEE | DBC | EUE | DK | *Kipling* |
| 91 53 0 472 006-2 | 92039 | ae | WGEE | DBC | DBR | DC | *Eugen Ionescu* |

# 3 Preserved locomotives

This section list all the locos classed as preserved including those which are owned by preservation groups for the supply of spare parts and unlikely to ever be restored.

Those locos owned by preservation groups but are main line registered and either on long-term hire to FOCs/TOCs or used for charter work or spot hire are included in section 1.

Names are listed even if the plates are not presently fitted because the loco is part way through overhaul.

Locos are listed at their home railway unless on a long term loan, but locos do move about and visit other railways or sites.

| Loco | previous numbers | key detail differences | livery | location | status | name |
|---|---|---|---|---|---|---|
| **Class 01** | | | | | | |
| D2953 | 11503 | o | GWS | PKR | OP | |
| D2956 | 11506 | o | BLK | ELR | OP | |

Note: Locos do not have train brakes

| Loco | previous numbers | key detail differences | livery | location | status | name |
|---|---|---|---|---|---|---|
| **Class 02** | | | | | | |
| | D2853 | vo | GWS | BH | OP | |
| | D2854 | vo | GWS | PKR | OP | |
| | D2858 | vo | GWS | MRB | UR | |
| | D2860 | vo | GWS | NRM | OP | |
| | D2866 | vo | BRW | PKR | UR | |
| | D2867 | vo | IND | BAT | OP | |
| | D2868 | vo | GWS | PKR | OP | |
| **Class 03** | | | | | | |
| 03018 | D2018 | vo | BRW | MRM | UR | |
| 03020 | D2020 | vo | BRW | MRM | SU | |
| 03022 | D2022 | vo | BRB | SCR | UR | |
| | D2023 | vo | GWS | KES | OP | |
| | D2024 | vo | IND | KES | SU | |
| 03027 | D2027 | vo | BRW | PKR | UR | |
| 03037 | D2037 | vo | BLK | RDR | SU | |
| | D2041 | vo | BLK | CVR | OP | |
| | D2046 | vo | IND | PVR | UR | |
| | D2051 | vo | GNY | NNR | SU | |
| 03059 | D2059 | xow | GWS | IWR | OP | |
| 03062 | D2062 | xow | GWS | ELR | OP | |
| 03063 | D2063 | xow | BRW | NNR | UR | |
| 03066 | D2066 | xow | BRW | BH | OP | |
| 03069 | D2069 | vo | GWS | VBR | UR | |
| 03072 | D2072 | vo | GWS | LHR | OP | |
| 03073 | D2073 | xow | BRW | RAC | OP | |
| 03078 | D2078 | xow | BLK | NTR | OP | |
| 03079 | D2079 | vo | BRW | DVR | OP | |
| 03081 | D2081 | vo | BRW | MRM | OP | |
| 03089 | D2089 | xow | GWS | MRM | OP | |
| 03090 | D2090 | vo | GNY | NRS | OP | |
| 03094 | D2094 | xow | GWS | RDR | OP | |
| 03099 | D2099 | vo | BRW | PKR | OP | |

Of the 20 Yorkshire Engine diesel-hydraulic Class 02s built, seven remain in preservation. D2854 is at Peak Rail. *Pip Dunn*

| | | | | | | |
|---|---|---|---|---|---|---|
| 03112 | D2112 | xow | GWS | RVR | OP | |
| 03113 | D2113 | vo | BRW | PKR | OP | |
| | D2117 | vo | MAR | LHR | OP | |
| 03118 | D2118 | vo | BRW | GCN | UR | |
| 03119 | D2119 | vo | IND | EOR | OP | |
| 03120 | D2120 | vo | GNY | FHR | OP | |
| | D2133 | vo | GWS | WSR | OP | |
| 03134 | D2134 | vo | IND | RDR | OP | |
| | D2138 | vo | GWS | MRB | OP | |
| | D2139 | vo | GNY | PKR | OP | |
| 03141 | D2141 | vo | IND | PBR | UR | |
| 03144 | D2144 | vo | BRW | WR | OP | |
| 03145 | D2145 | vo | BRW | MOL | OP | |
| | D2148 | vo | GWS | RSR | UR | |
| 03152 | D2152 | vo | GRE | SCR | OP | |
| 03158 | D2158 | xow | GWS | TIT | OP | *MARGARET-ANN* |
| 03162 | D2162 | xow | BRW | LLR | UR | |
| 03170 | D2170 | xow | BRW | EOR | OP | |
| | D2178 | vo | GWS | GIR | OP | |
| 03179 | D2179 | xo | UND | RHR | UR | |
| 03180 | D2180 | xow | BRW | PKR | SU | |
| | D2182 | vo | GRN | GWR | OP | |
| | D2184 | vo | BLK | CVR | OP | |
| 03189 | D2189 | vo | BRW | RSR | OP | |
| | D2192 | vo | BLK | PDR | OP | *TITAN* |
| 03197 | D2197 | xow | BRW | MRM | UR | |
| | D2199 | xow | GWS | PKR | OP | |
| 03371 | D2371 | xow | BRW | PDR | OP | |
| 03399 | D2399 | xow | BRW | MRM | OP | |
| 03901 | D2128, 03128 | xo | BLK | PKR | OP | |

Note: 03079/119/120/141/144/145/152/179 have reduced height cabs

The Class 03 diesel mechanical 0-6-0 shunters were BR's preferred small shunter design but all have been retired and several are preserved. Immaculate 03081 rests at Mangapps Railway Museum on 25 August 2012. *Pip Dunn*

## Class 04

| | | | | | |
|---|---|---|---|---|---|
| | D2203 | vo | GNY | EBR | OP |
| | D2205 | vo | GSW | PKR | OP |
| | D2207 | vo | GWS | NYM | UR |
| | D2229 | vo | GRE | PR | SU |
| | D2245 | vo | GWS | DVR | OP |
| | D2246 | vo | GWS | SDR | OP |
| | D2271 | vo | IND | WSR | SU |
| | D2272 | vo | GRE | PKR | UR |
| | D2279 | vo | BLK | PKR | OP |
| | D2280 | vo | BLK | NNR | SU |
| | D2284 | vo | GWS | PR | OP |
| | D2298 | vo | GNY | BRC | OP |
| | D2302 | vo | GWS | MOL | OP |
| 04110 | D2310 | vo | BRW | BAT | OP |
| | D2324 | vo | IND | BU | SU |
| | D2325 | vo | GWS | MRM | OP |
| | D2334 | vo | GWS | MNR | OP |
| | D2337 | vo | GWS | PKR | OP |

## Class 05

| | | | | | |
|---|---|---|---|---|---|
| 05001 | D2554, 97803 | vo | GWS | IWR | OP |
| | D2578 | vo | GWS | MOL | OP |
| | D2587 | vo | GWS | PKR | UR |
| | D2595 | vo | GWS | RSR | OP |

Class 04 D2325 passes 03197 at Mangapps Railway Musuem. The Class 04s were built by Drewry and had the same Gardner engines as their BR equivalents. *Pip Dunn*

Just one Class 06 survives out of the original 35 locos, 06003 which is preserved at Peak Rail. *Pip Dunn*

Seven of the 14 Class 07s survive, two in industry and five preserved. One of the latter is 07012, which spent a period based at Scunthorpe steelworks, where it rests on shed on 18 April 2015. *Pip Dunn*

## Class 06

| | | | | | | |
|---|---|---|---|---|---|---|
| 06003 | D2420, 97804 | vo | BRW | PR | OP | |

## Class 07

| | | | | | | |
|---|---|---|---|---|---|---|
| 07001 | D2985 | xow | BRW | PKR | OP | |
| 07005 | D2989 | xow | IND | WH | SU | |
| 07010 | D2994 | vo | BRW | AVR | OP | |
| 07012 | D2996 | vo | BRW | BH | OP | |
| 07013 | D2997 | xow | BRW | ELR | SU | |

## Class 08

| | | | | | | |
|---|---|---|---|---|---|---|
| | D3000 | vo | GNY | PKR | UR | |
| | D3002 | vo | BLK | PVR | OP | |
| | D3014 | vo | BRW | PDR | OP | *SAMSON* |
| 08011 | D3018 | vo | GWS | CPR | OP | *HAVERSHAM* |
| | D3019 | vo | UND | CRT | UR | |
| 08015 | D3022 | vo | GWS | SVR | OP | |
| 08016 | D3023 | vo | BRW | PKR | OP | |
| 08022 | D3030 | vo | IND | CWR | OP | *LION* |
| 08032 | D3044 | vo | BRW | MHR | OP | *MENDIP* |
| 08046 | D3059 | vo | BRW | CAL | OP | *BRECHIN CITY* |
| 08054 | D3067 | vo | BRB | EBR | UR | |
| 08060 | D3074 | vo | IND | CWR | OP | *UNICORN* |
| 08064 | D3079 | vo | BLK | NRS | UR | |

| | | | | | | |
|---|---|---|---|---|---|---|
| | D3101 | vo | BLK | GCR | OP | |
| 08102 | D3167 | vo | GWS | LWR | OP | |
| 08108 | D3174 | vo | BLK | KES | OP | *Dover Castle* |
| 08114 | D3180 | vo | GRE | GCN | OP | |
| 08123 | D3190 | vo | GRE | CWR | OP | |
| 08133 | D3201 | vo | GWS | SVR | OP | |
| 08164 | D3232 | vo | BRW | ELR | OP | *PRUDENCE* |
| | D3255 | vo | UND | MAL | UR | |
| | D3261 | vo | BLK | SCR | OP | |
| 08195 | D3265 | vo | BLK | LLR | OP | |
| 08202 | D3272 | vo | BRW | AVR | OP | |
| 08238 | D3308 | vo | BRW | DFR | OP | *Charlie* |
| 08266 | D3336 | vo | DEP | KWV | OP | |
| 08288 | D3358 | vo | BLK | MHR | OP | |
| 08331 | D3401 | ao | BLK | MRB | OP | |
| 08359 | D3429 | vo | GWS | TSR | OP | |
| 08377 | D3462 | vo | GWS | WSR | OP | |
| 08436 | D3551 | xo | BLK | SWR | OP | |
| 08443 | D3558 | vo | GWS | BKR | OP | |
| 08444 | D3559 | vo | GWS | BWR | OP | |
| 08471 | D3586 | vo | GWS | SVR | OP | |
| 08473 | D3588 | vo | BRW | DFR | SU | |
| 08476 | D3591 | vo | BLK | SWR | OP | |
| 08479 | D3594 | vo | BRW | ELR | OP | |
| 08490 | D3605 | vo | BLK | STR | OP | |
| 08495 | D3610 | xo | BRW | NYM | UR | |
| 08528 | D3690 | xo | GWS | GCR | OP | |
| 08556 | D3723 | vo | GWS | NYM | OP | |
| 08590 | D3757 | xo | BRW | MRB | OP | |
| 08598 | D3765 | ao | POT | CHR | OP | |
| 08604 | D3771 | vo | BRW | DRC | OP | *PHANTOM* |
| 08633 | D3800 | ao | EWS | CHV | UR | |
| 08635 | D3802 | xo | BRW | SVR | UR | |
| 08694 | D3861 | xo | EWS | GCR | UR | |
| 08757 | D3925 | ao | RES | TBR | UR | |
| 08767 | D3935 | xo | GWS | NNR | SU | |
| 08769 | D3937 | vo | GWS | SVR | OP | *Gladys* |
| 08772 | D3940 | xo | GWS | NNR | OP | |
| 08773 | D3941 | xo | BRW | EBR | OP | |
| 08784 | D3952 | ao | EWS | GCN | OP | |
| 08825 | D3993 | xo | BRW | CPR | OP | |
| 08830 | D3998 | xow | BLK | PKR | OP | |
| 08850 | D4018 | xow | BRB | NYM | OP | |
| 08881 | D4095 | ao | GWS | SDR | OP | |
| 08888 | D4118 | ao | EWS | KES | OP | |
| 08896 | D4126 | xo | EWS | SVR | SU | |
| 08907 | D4137 | ao | DBS | GCR | OP | |
| 08911 | D4141 | xo | NRM | NRM | OP | *MATEY* |
| 08915 | D4145 | xo | BLK | NTR | OP | |
| 08922 | D4152 | ao | EWS | GCN | OP | |
| 08937 | D4167 | xo | GWS | DAR | OP | *BLUEBELL MEL* |
| 08993 | D3759, 08592 | xo | EWS | KWV | OP | *ASHBURNHAM* |
| 08995 | D3854, 08687 | ao | EWS | WIS | UR | |

Note: 08993-995 have reduced bodyheight
08633 has a swinghead coupler

## Class 09

| | | | | | | |
|---|---|---|---|---|---|---|
| 09001 | D3665 | xow | EWS | PKR | OP | |
| 09004 | D3668 | xow | BRW | SCR | UR | |
| 09010 | D3721 | xow | GWS | SDR | OP | |
| 09012 | D4100 | xow | GWS | SVR | UR | *Dick Hardy* |
| 09015 | D4103 | xo | DEP | WIS | SU | |
| 09017 | D4105 | xo | NRM | NRM | OP | |
| 09018 | D4106 | xow | GWS | BLU | OP | |
| 09019 | D4107 | xow | GWS | WSR | OP | |
| 09024 | D4112 | xo | DEP | ELR | OP | |
| 09025 | D4113 | xo | GWS | EKR | OP | |
| 09026 | D4114 | aow | GWS | SPA | OP | *Cedric Wares* |
| 09107 | D4013, 08845 | aow | EWS | SVR | UR | |

## Class 10

| | | | | | | |
|---|---|---|---|---|---|---|
| | D3452 | vo | BLK | BWR | OP | |
| | D3489 | xo | BLK | SPA | OP | *COLONEL TOMLINE* |
| 10119 | D4067 | vo | BRW | GCR | OP | *Margaret Ethel – Thomas Alfred Naylor* |
| | D4092 | vo | GWS | BH | UR | |

## Class 11

| | | | | | |
|---|---|---|---|---|---|
| | 12052 | vo | IND | CAL | SU |
| | 12077 | vo | GWS | MRB | OP |
| | 12082 | xo | GWS | MHR | OP |
| | 12083 | vo | BLE | BAT | SU |
| | 12088 | vo | GWS | ALN | OP |
| | 12093 | vo | GWS | CAL | OP |
| | 12099 | vo | BLK | SVR | OP |
| | 12131 | vo | BLK | NNR | OP |

## Class 12

| | | | | | |
|---|---|---|---|---|---|
| | 15224 | vo | GWS | SPA | OP |

## Unclassified locos

| | | | | | |
|---|---|---|---|---|---|
| | D2511 | vo | GWS | KWV | OP |
| | D2767 | vo | GWS | BKR | OP |
| | D2774 | vo | GWS | STR | OP |
| | 18000 | vo | GWR | DRC | SU |

## Class 14

| | | | | | |
|---|---|---|---|---|---|
| | D9500 | vo | GWS | PKR | UR |
| | D9502 | vo | GWS | ELR | UR |
| | D9504 | xo | GWS | KES | OP |
| | D9513 | vo | NCB | EBR | OP |
| | D9516 | xo | GWS | DRC | OP |
| | D9518 | vo | NCB | WSR | UR |
| | D9520 | xo | GWS | NVR | OP |
| | D9521 | vo | GWS | DFR | OP |
| | D9523 | xo | MWS | WEN | OP |
| 14901 | D9524 | xo | BLU | CVR | OP |

| | | | | | | |
|---|---|---|---|---|---|---|
| | D9525 | vo | GWS | PKR | SU | |
| | D9526 | vo | GWS | WSR | OP | |
| 14029 | D9529 | xo | BRB | NVR | OP | |
| | D9531 | xo | GWS | ELR | OP | *ERNEST* |
| | D9537 | vo | DSY | ELR | OP | |
| | D9539 | vo | GWS | RSR | OP | |
| | D9551 | vo | GOP | SVR | OP | |
| | D9553 | vo | GWS | VBR | SU | |
| | D9555 | vo | GWS | DFR | OP | |

## Class 15

| | | | | | |
|---|---|---|---|---|---|
| DB968000 | D8233 | vo | GYP | ELR | UR |

Note: loco has a through steam pipe

## Class 17

| | | | | | |
|---|---|---|---|---|---|
| | D8568 | vo | GFY | CPR | OP |

Note: loco has a through steam pipe

## Class 20

| | | | | | |
|---|---|---|---|---|---|
| 20001 | D8001 | xo | GFY | MRB | OP |
| 20020 | D8020 | xo | BRB | BKR | UR |
| 20031 | D8031 | xop | TLC | KWV | OP |
| 20035 | D8035, CFD2001 | ao | CFD | GWR | SU |
| 20048 | D8048 | xo | BRB | MRB | UR |
| 20050 | D8000 | vo | GNY | NRM | UR |

The Class 14s had very short BR lives but excelled in industry and are now popular attractions at preserved railways. D9537, in Desert Sand livery, pauses at Ramsbottom having arrived with the 0900 from Bury Bolton Street on 8 July 2017. *Pip Dunn*

| | | | | | | |
|---|---|---|---|---|---|---|
| 20057 | D8057 | xo | GYP | MRB | UR | |
| 20059 | D8059 | xo | GYP | MRB | OP | |
| 20063 | D8063 | xo | CFD | BAT | UR | |
| 20098 | D8098 | xop | GNY | GCR | OP | |
| 20137 | D8137 | xop | GFY | GWR | OP | |
| 20154 | D8154 | xop | BRB | GCN | UR | |
| 20169 | D8169 | xop | UND | WEN | UR | |
| 20188 | D8188 | xop | GYP | MRB | OP | |
| 20214 | D8314 | xop | GYP | LHR | OP | |
| 20228 | D8128 | xop | BRB | BIR | UR | |

Note: 20050 has a through steam pipe

## Class 23

| | | | | | | |
|---|---|---|---|---|---|---|
| | D5910 | xo | UND | BH | UC | |

Note: This is a new build loco still under construction. It uses parts of the bodyshell of 37372 (D6859, 37159) which is now regarded as disposed of.

## Class 24

| | | | | | | |
|---|---|---|---|---|---|---|
| 24032 | D5032 | vi | GYP | NYM | UR | |
| 24054 | D5054, TDB968008 | vb | GYP | ELR | UR | *PHIL SOUTHERN* |
| 24061 | D5061, RDB968007, 97201 | vb | GNY | NYM | UR | |
| 24081 | D5081 | vo | BRB | GWR | UR | |

Of 117 Class 17 Bo-Bo Type 1s built by Clayton for BR, just one survives, D8568. The loco is a popular guest for heritage railway events and on 2 October 2015 it stands at Bridgnorth with the 1608 to Kidderminster. *Pip Dunn*

## Class 25

| | | | | | | |
|---|---|---|---|---|---|---|
| 25035 | D5185 | xip | GYP | GCR | OP | |
| 25057 | D5207 | xbp | BRB | NNR | UR | |
| 25059 | D5209 | xbp | BRB | KWV | OP | |
| 25067 | D5217 | vb | GYP | BU | SU | |
| 25072 | D5222 | xi | GFY | CAL | SU | |
| 25083 | D5233 | vip | BRB | CAL | SU | |
| 25173 | D7523 | xo | GYP | BAT | UR | |
| 25185 | D7535 | xo | BYP | PDR | OP | *MERCURY* |
| 25191 | D7541 | xop | GYP | SDR | UR | |
| 25235 | D7585 | xip | BRB | BKR | UR | |
| 25244 | D7594 | xop | UND | KES | SU | |
| 25262 | D7612, 25901 | xo | GYP | SDR | | |
| 25265 | D7615 | xo | BRB | BU | UR | |
| 25279 | D7629 | xo | GYP | GCN | OP | |
| 25283 | D7633, 25904 | xop | GYP | DFR | UR | |
| 25309 | D7659, 25909 | xo | GYP | PKR | SU | |
| 25313 | D7663 | xop | BRB | WEN | SU | |
| 25321 | D7671 | xop | GYP | MRB | OP | |
| 25322 | D7672, 25912 | xop | BRU | CHV | UR | *TAMWORTH CASTLE* |

## Class 26

| | | | | | | |
|---|---|---|---|---|---|---|
| 26001 | D5301 | xo | GNY | LHR | OP | |
| 26002 | D5302 | xo | GNY | STR | SU | |
| 26004 | D5304 | xo | TLC | BU | SU | |
| 26007 | D5300 | xo | BRB | BH | UR | |
| 26010 | D5310 | xo | GFY | LLR | OP | |
| 26011 | D5311 | xo | BRB | BU | SU | |
| 26014 | D5314 | xo | GNY | CAL | OP | |
| 26024 | D5324 | xop | BRB | BKR | UR | |
| 26025 | D5325 | xop | GNY | STR | SU | |
| 26035 | D5335 | xop | BRB | CAL | SU | |
| 26038 | D5338 | xop | BRB | NYM | OP | *Tom Clift 1954-2012* |
| 26040 | D5340 | xop | BRB | WAV | UR | |
| 26043 | D5343 | xop | BRB | GWR | OP | |

## Class 27

| | | | | | |
|---|---|---|---|---|---|
| 27001 | D5347 | xip | BRB | BKR | OP |
| 27005 | D5351 | xip | BRB | BKR | UR |
| 27007 | D5353 | vop | UND | MHR | SU |
| 27024 | D5370, ADB968028 | xop | GYP | CAL | OP |
| 27050 | D5394, 27106 | xip | GNY | STR | OP |
| 27056 | D5401, 27112 | xip | GFY | GCR | UR |
| 27059 | D5410, 27123, 27205 | xotp | UND | ESR | UR |
| 27066 | D5386, 27103, 27212 | xotp | BRB | BH | UR |

## Class 28

| | | | | | |
|---|---|---|---|---|---|
| D5705 | ADB968006, S15705 | vo | GYP | ELR | UR |

Class 26 D5343 is based at the Gloucestershire Warwickshire Railway but has visited several other heritage lines, and on 9 September 2017 it runs round at Leicester North having arrived with the 0945 from Loughborough during a visit to the Great Central Railway. *Pip Dunn*

Class 27 5401 arrives are Rothley on 20 March 2016 with the 1500 Loughborough-Leicester North. This loco was numbered 27112 and then 27056 during its BR career. *Pip Dunn*

31162 crossing the A684 at Leeming Bar with a train for Redmire on 18 July 2015 during its visit to the Wensleydale Railway. *Pip Dunn*

## Class 31

| | | | | | | |
|---|---|---|---|---|---|---|
| 31018 | D5500 | vi | BRB | NRM | SU | |
| 31101 | D5518 | xo | BRB | AVR | OP | |
| 31108 | D5526 | xop | RFO | MRB | OP | |
| 31119 | D5537 | xo | BRB | EBR | SU | |
| 31130 | D5548 | xop | RFO | AVR | OP | |
| 31162 | D5580 | xi | BRB | MRB | OP | |
| 31163 | D5581 | xo | GYP | CPR | OP | |
| 31203 | D5627 | xo | GNY | PBR | OP | *Steve Ogden GM* |
| 31206 | D5630 | xo | CCE | RHR | OP | |
| 31207 | D5631 | xo | GNY | NNR | UR | |
| 31210 | D5634 | xop | RFO | DFR | UR | |
| 31270 | D5800 | xop | REG | PKR | OP | *Athena* |
| 31271 | D5801 | xop | TLA | NVR | OP | *Stratford 1840-2001* |
| 31289 | D5821 | xo | EBP | RHR | OP | *PHŒNIX* |
| 31327 | D5862 | xo | GYP | STR | OP | |
| 31414 | D5814 | xe | GYP | BH | UR | |
| 31418 | D5522 | xei | BRB | MRB | UR | |
| 31430 | D5695, 31265, 31530 | xy | BRB | MRM | OP | *Sister Dora* |
| 31435 | D5600, 31179 | xe | GYE | EBR | SU | |
| 31438 | D5557, 31139, 31538 | xe | BRB | EOR | OP | |
| 31466 | D5533, 31115 | xe | EWS | DFR | OP | |
| 31563 | D5830, 31297, 31463 | xy | GOP | GCR | OP | |

In BR General grey colours, 33110, based at the Bodmin and Wenford Railway, waits at Bodmin Parkway with a train for Bodmin General on 24 June 2011. The loco was one of 19 Class 33/0s converted for push-pull use. *Pip Dunn*

## Class 33

| | | | | | | |
|---|---|---|---|---|---|---|
| 33002 | D6501 | xyp | GNY | SDR | OP | |
| 33008 | D6508 | xyp | GYP | BAT | UR | *Eastleigh* |
| 33018 | D6530 | xyp | BRB | MRM | UR | |
| 33019 | D6534 | xyp | DUT | BAT | UR | *Griffon* |
| 33021 | D6539 | xyp | BRB | CHV | UR | *Captain Charles* |
| 33035 | D6553 | xyp | BRB | BH | OP | |
| 33046 | D6564 | xyp | SWT | ELR | SU | |
| 33048 | D6566 | xyp | GYP | WSR | UR | |
| 33052 | D6570 | xyp | GNY | KES | SU | *Ashford* |
| 33053 | D6571 | xyp | BRB | MHR | OP | |
| 33057 | D6575 | xep | GYP | WSR | OP | |
| 33063 | D6583 | xep | TMF | SPA | OP | *RJ Mitchell – DESIGNER OF THE SPITFIRE* |
| 33065 | D6585 | xep | BRB | SPA | UR | *Sealion* |
| 33102 | D6513 | xew | BRB | CHV | UR | *Sophie* |
| 33103 | D6514 | xewp | BRB | EVR | OP | *SWORDFISH* |
| 33108 | D6521 | xew | BRB | SVR | OP | |
| 33109 | D6525 | xew | DEP | ELR | OP | *Captain Bill Smith RNR* |
| 33110 | D6527 | xew | DEP | BWR | OP | |
| 33111 | D6528 | xew | BRB | SWR | OP | |
| 33116 | D6535 | xewp | BRB | GCR | OP | |
| 33117 | D6536 | xew | BRB | ELR | UR | |
| 33201 | D6586 | xesp | BRB | SWR | OP | |
| 33202 | D6587 | xesp | BRB | MRM | OP | *Dennis G. Robinson* |
| 33208 | D6593 | xesp | GYP | BAT | UR | |

One of four surviving Class 35 Hymek diesel-hydraulic Type 3s, D7076 runs round at Rawtenstall ready to work the 1336 to Heywood on 8 July 2017. *Pip Dunn*

## Class 35

| | | | | | | |
|---|---|---|---|---|---|---|
| | D7017 | vop | GYP | WSR | OP | |
| | D7018 | vop | GYP | WSR | UR | |
| | D7029 | vop | BRB | SVR | UR | |
| | D7076 | vbp | BRB | ELR | OP | |

## Class 37

| | | | | | | |
|---|---|---|---|---|---|---|
| 37003 | D6703 | xot | BRB | LR | UR | |
| 37009 | D6709, 37340 | xot | BRB | GCR | UR | |
| 37023 | D6723 | xo | UND | ALL | UR | |
| 37029 | D6729 | xot | GYP | EOR | OP | |
| 37032 | D6732, 37353 | xot | GYP | NNR | UR | |
| 37037 | D6737, 37321 | xip | BRB | SDR | UR | |
| 37042 | D6742 | xot | EWS | EDR | SU | |
| 37075 | D6775 | xop | TTG | KWV | OP | |
| 37097 | D6797 | xo | BRB | CAL | SU | *Old Fettercairn* |
| 37108 | D6808, 37325 | xip | BRB | RAC | UR | |
| 37109 | D6809 | xo | BRB | ELR | OP | |
| 37142 | D6842 | xop | BRB | BWR | OP | |
| 37152 | D6852, 37310 | xop | RSR | PKR | UR | |
| 37190 | D6890, 37314 | xip | BRB | MRB | UR | |
| 37214 | D6914 | xotp | WCR | BKR | SU | |
| 37215 | D6915 | xotp | BRB | GWR | OP | |

| | | | | | | |
|---|---|---|---|---|---|---|
| 37216 | D6916 | xotp | GYP | PBR | UR | |
| 37227 | D6927 | xotp | TTG | BU | UR | |
| 37240 | D6940 | xotp | BRB | LLR | OP | |
| 37248 | D6948 | xotp | GYP | GWR | OP | |
| 37250 | D6950 | xotp | TRN | WEN | UR | |
| 37261 | D6961 | xip | DRC | BKR | UR | |
| 37263 | D6963 | xop | BRB | TSR | UR | |
| 37264 | D6964 | xip | LLB | NYM | OP | |
| 37275 | D6975 | xotp | BRB | SDR | OP | |
| 37294 | D6994 | xotp | BRB | EBR | OP | |
| 37308 | D6608 | xotp | UND | DFR | UR | |
| 37350 | D6700, 37119 | xot | GYP | NRM | UR | |
| 37521 | D6817, 37117 | xotp | UND | BH | UR | |
| 37674 | D6869, 37169 | xotp | RSR | WEN | UR | |
| 37679 | D6823, 37123 | xotp | TTG | ELR | SU | |
| 37688 | D6905, 37205 | xotp | DRU | MNR | OP | |
| 37703 | D6767, 37067 | xotp | DRU | BKR | OP | |
| 37714 | D6724, 37024 | xotp | TLM | GCR | OP | *Cardiff Canton* |

## Class 40

| | | | | | | |
|---|---|---|---|---|---|---|
| 40012 | D212, 97407 | xi | BRB | BH | UR | *AUREOL* |
| 40013 | D213 | xo | GYP | BH | OP | *ANDANIA* |
| 40106 | D306 | vb | GFY | ELR | OP | *ATLANTIC CONVEYOR* |
| 40118 | D318, 97408 | xi | BRB | TRM | UR | |
| 40122 | D200 | xi | GNY | NRM | SU | |
| 40135 | D335, 97406 | xb | BRB | ELR | OP | |

Seven Class 40s survive out of a fleet of 200, and one is D213 *Andania*. On 18 June 2016 it has just arrived with the 1357 Grosmont-Pickering and it runs round ready to take out the 1531 back to Grosmont. *Pip Dunn*

1A12

## Class 41

| | | | | | | |
|---|---|---|---|---|---|---|
| 41001 | 43000, ADB975812 | ae | BRP | GCN | OP | |

## Class 42

| | | | | | | |
|---|---|---|---|---|---|---|
| | D821 | vi | MYP | SVR | UR | *GREYHOUND* |
| | D832 | vb | GYP | ELR | OP | *ONSLAUGHT* |

## Class 44

| | | | | | | |
|---|---|---|---|---|---|---|
| 44004 | D4 | vo | GNY | MRB | OP | *GREAT GABLE* |
| 44008 | D8 | vo | GYP | PKR | OP | *PENYGHENT* |

## Class 45

| | | | | | | |
|---|---|---|---|---|---|---|
| 45015 | D14 | xo | BRB | BAT | SU | |
| 45041 | D53 | xi | BRB | MRB | OP | *ROYAL TANK REGIMENT* |
| 45060 | D100 | xi | BRB | BH | OP | *SHERWOOD FORESTER* |
| 45105 | D86 | xe | BRB | BH | UR | |
| 45108 | D120 | xe | BRB | ELR | OP | |
| 45112 | D61 | xe | BRB | BU | SU | *ROYAL ARMY ORDNACE CORPS* |

*Opposite:* Warship D832 *Onslaught* leads Hymek D7076 on the 1336 Rawtenstall-Heywood on 8 July 2017. D832 is one of just two Class 42s which are preserved. *Pip Dunn*

The first generation of Peaks was the pilot scheme Class 44s. D8 *Penyghent* stands at Holt on 16 June 2017 having arrived from Sheringham. *Anthony Hicks*

Arriving at Winchcombe on 29 July 2017 is 45149 on a Toddington-Cheltenham Racecourse train. A dozen Class 45s survive but only five were operational in 2017. *Pip Dunn*

| | | | | | | |
|---|---|---|---|---|---|---|
| 45118 | D67 | xe | BRB | RTC | SU | *ROYAL ARTILLERYMAN* |
| 45125 | D123 | xe | GYP | GCR | UR | *LEICESTERSHIRE AND DERBYSHIRE YEOMANRY* |
| 45132 | D22 | xe | BRB | EOR | UR | |
| 45133 | D40 | xe | BRB | NNR | OP | |
| 45135 | D99 | xe | BRB | ELR | SU | *3RD CARABINIER* |
| 45149 | D135 | xe | BRB | GWR | OP | |

## Class 46

| | | | | | |
|---|---|---|---|---|---|
| 46010 | D147 | xo | BRB | GCR | UR |
| 46035 | D172, 97403 | xo | BRB | PKR | SU |
| 46045 | D182, 97404 | xb | BYP | MRB | OP |

## Class 47

| | | | | | | |
|---|---|---|---|---|---|---|
| 47004 | D1524 | xip | GYP | EBR | SU | |
| 47105 | D1693 | xb | BRB | GWR | UR | |
| 47117 | D1705 | xip | BRB | GCR | OP | *SPARROWHAWK* |
| 47192 | D1842 | xo | GFY | RAC | OP | |
| 47205 | D1855, 47395 | aotm | RFD | NLR | OP | |
| 47292 | D1994 | xotm | BLL | GCN | OP | |
| 47306 | D1787 | xotm | RFE | BWR | UR | *The Sapper* |
| 47367 | D1886 | xos | BRB | MNR | OP | *KENNY COCKBIRD* |
| 47376 | D1895 | xos | FTT | GWR | OP | *Freightliner 1995* |
| 47401 | D1500 | xe | BRB | MRB | OP | *North Eastern* |
| 47402 | D1501 | xe | GYP | ELR | OP | |
| 47417 | D1516 | xei | GYP | MRB | UR | |
| 47449 | D1566 | xe | BRB | LLR | OP | |

Class 46 D182 waits at Bewdley on 20 May 2016 with the 0855 to Kidderminster during the loco's visit to the Severn Valley Railway. The loco sports the BR blue but with small yellow panels, a livery not seen on the type in BR days. *Pip Dunn*

47579 *James Nightall GC* is based at the Mangapps Railway Museum, where it was pictured after its return to service on 25 August 2012. The loco is to have its vacuum brake capability restored at the Mid Hants Railway, where it will stay for three years. *Pip Dunn*

| | | | | | | |
|---|---|---|---|---|---|---|
| 47484 | D1662 | xe | GWR | WIS | UR | *ISAMBARD KINGDOM BRUNEL* |
| 47524 | D1107 | xe | RES | CHV | UR | |
| 47579 | D1778, 47183, 47793 | aet | BRE | MHR | OP | *James Nightall GC* |
| 47596 | D1933, 47255 | xe | NSD | MNR | OP | *Aldeburgh Festival* |
| 47635 | D1606, 47029 | xe | LLB | EOR | OP | *Jimmy Milne* |
| 47640 | D1921, 47244 | xe | LLB | BAT | UR | *University of Strathclyde* |
| 47643 | D1970, 47269 | xep | IOS | BKR | OP | |
| 47712 | D1948, 47505 | xet | SCR | RAC | OP | *Lady Diana Spencer* |
| 47761 | D1619, 47038, 47564 | aet | RES | MRB | SU | |
| 47765 | D1643, 47059, 47631 | xet | SCR | GCN | OP | |
| 47771 | D1946, 47503 | aet | RES | ZG | UR | |
| 47785 | D1909, 47232, 47665, 47820 | xet | EWS | WEN | SU | |
| 47799 | D1654, 47070, 47620, 47835 | aet | ROY | EDR | UR | *Prince Henry* |
| 47828 | D1966, 47266, 47629 | aet | ICS | DR | OP | |
| 47840 | D1661, 47077, 47613 | xet | GYP | WSR | OP | *NORTH STAR* |

## Class 50

| | | | | | | |
|---|---|---|---|---|---|---|
| 50002 | D402 | xep | BRB | SDR | UR | |
| 50015 | D415 | xep | LLB | ELR | OP | *Valiant* |
| 50019 | D419 | xep | LLB | MNR | UR | *Ramillies* |
| 50021 | D421 | xep | LLB | ZG | UR | *Rodney* |
| 50026 | D426 | xep | NSD | ZG | OP | *Indomitable* |
| 50027 | D427 | xep | NSR | MHR | OP | *Lion* |
| 50029 | D429 | xep | LLB | PKR | SU | *Renown* |
| 50030 | D430 | xep | LLB | PKR | UR | *Repulse* |
| 50031 | D431 | xep | ICS | SVR | OP | *Hood* |
| 50033 | D433 | xep | LLB | TRM | SU | *Glorious* |
| 50035 | D435 | xep | BRB | SVR | OP | *Ark Royal* |
| 50042 | D442 | xep | LLB | BWR | OP | *Triumph* |

## Class 52

| | | | | | | |
|---|---|---|---|---|---|---|
| | D1010 | xo | MYP | WSR | OP | *WESTERN CAMPAIGNER* |
| | D1013 | xo | BRB | SVR | UR | *WESTERN RANGER* |
| | D1023 | xi | BRB | NRM | SU | *WESTERN FUSILIER* |
| | D1041 | xo | BRB | ELR | UR | *WESTERN PRINCE* |
| | D1048 | xo | BRB | MRB | UR | *WESTERN LADY* |
| | D1062 | xo | BRB | SVR | OP | *WESTERN COURIER* |

## Class 55

| | | | | | | |
|---|---|---|---|---|---|---|
| 55015 | D9015 | xe | GYP | BH | UR | *TULYAR* |
| 55016 | D9016 | xei | GYP | WWH | UR | *GORDON HIGHLANDER* |
| 55019 | D9019 | xe | BRB | BH | OP | *ROYAL HIGHLAND FUSILIER* |

## Class 56

| | | | | | | |
|---|---|---|---|---|---|---|
| 56006 | | aos | BRB | ELR | OP | |
| 56097 | | aos | TLC | GCN | UR | |

50026 *Indomitable* has been a visitor to many heritage railways since it came back in to use in 2012 after a 20-year restoration. On 10 June 2016 it has just arrived at Holt on the 1353 from Sheringham. The loco sports the final, darker, version of the Network SouthEast livery. *Pip Dunn*

All Class 52s have spent twice as long in preservation than they did with BR. D1010 *Western Campaigner* stands at Crowcombe Heathfield on the West Somerset Railway which has been its home since January 1991. *Anthony Hicks*

56097 stands at Ruddington on 6 October 2012. This is one of just three preserved Class 56s, one of which is main line registered, although other examples survive in Hungary and with spot hire companies. *Pip Dunn*

## Class 58

| | | | | |
|---|---|---|---|---|
| 58012 | aosp | TMF | BAT | SU |
| 58016 | aosp | FER | LR | UR |
| 58022 | aosp | TMF | PKR | SU |
| 58023 | aosp | MLB | BAT | UR |
| 58048 | aosp | EWS | BAT | SU |

# Main line electric locos

| Last number | Previous official numbers carried | Key detail differences | Livery | Location | Status | Current name |
|---|---|---|---|---|---|---|
| **Class 71** | | | | | | |
| 71001 | E5001 | xe | GYP | NRS | SU | |
| **Class 73** | | | | | | |
| 73001 | E6001, 73901 | xew | BRB | DFR | OP | |
| 73002 | E6002 | xew | LLB | DFR | SU | |
| 73003 | E6003 | xew | GYP | SCR | OP | *Sir Herbert Walker* |
| 73114 | E6020 | xew | LLB | BAT | UR | |
| 73118 | E6024 | xewl | EUS | BIR | OP | |
| 73129 | E6036 | xew | EBP | GWR | OP | |
| 73130 | E6037 | xewl | EUS | FIN | OP | |
| 73140 | E6047 | xew | NSR | SPA | OP | |
| 73210 | E6022, 73116 | xew | IGX | MNR | UR | *Selhurst* |
| **Class 76** | | | | | | |
| 76020 | E26020 | vo | BLK | NRM | SU | |
| **Class 77** | | | | | | |
| 1502 | E27000 | ae | BLK | MRB | SU | *ELECTRA* |
| 1505 | E27001 | ae | DNS | MSIM | SU | *ARIADNE* |
| 1501 | E27003 | ae | DNS | TIL | OP | *DIANA* |
| **Class 81** | | | | | | |
| 81002 | E3003 | xe | BRB | BH | SU | |
| **Class 82** | | | | | | |
| 82008 | E3054 | xe | ICO | BH | SU | |
| **Class 83** | | | | | | |
| 83012 | E3035 | xe | EBY | BH | SU | |
| **Class 84** | | | | | | |
| 84001 | E3036 | xe | BRB | BH | SU | |
| **Class 85** | | | | | | |
| 85006 | E3061, 85101 | xe | BRB | BH | SU | |
| **Class 87** | | | | | | |
| 87001 | | ae | BRB | NRM | SU | *Stephenson* |
| 87035 | | ae | BRB | RAC | SU | *Robert Burns* |
| **Class 89** | | | | | | |
| 89001 | | ae | ICO | BH | SU | |

# 4 Disposed locomotives

This part of the book lists all locos that were owned or leased by BR and subsequent private TOCs/FOCs but have since been scrapped. They are listed by their last number carried, and all previous numbers are detailed, with the most recent number(s) applied before the last number. Some locos, such as Class 31/5s and 47/8s, carried the same TOPS number twice. Locos owned by the 'Big four' that were withdrawn before nationalisation are not included.

All pre-TOPS numbers on diesels were initially prefixed D, which may or may not have been removed and so are excluded. Any allocated TOPS numbers which were allocated or intended, but not applied are not listed.

Industrial shunting locos registered in the 015xx series are not detailed.

**Unclassified LMS shunters**

| | |
|---|---|
| | 7055 |
| | 7056 |
| 7408 | 7058 |

**Unclassified shunter diesel-mechanical 0-4-0**

| | |
|---|---|
| 2400 | 11177 |
| 2401 | 11178 |
| 2402 | 11179 |
| 2403 | 11180 |
| 2404 | 11181 |
| 2405 | 11182 |
| 2406 | 11183 |
| 2407 | 11184 |
| 2408 | 11185 |
| 2409 | 11186 |

**Unclassified shunter diesel-mechanical 0-4-0**

| | |
|---|---|
| 2500 | 11116 |
| 2501 | 11117 |
| 2502 | 11118 |
| 2503 | 11119 |
| 2504 | 11120 |
| 2505 | 11144 |
| 2506 | 11145 |
| 2507 | 11146 |
| 2508 | 11147 |
| 2509 | 11148 |
| 2510 | |
| 2512 | |
| 2513 | |
| 2514 | |
| 2515 | |
| 2516 | |
| 2517 | |
| 2518 | |
| 2519 | |

**Unclassified shunter diesel-hydraulic 0-4-0**

| | |
|---|---|
| 2700 | 11700 |
| 2701 | 11701 |
| 2702 | 11702 |
| 2703 | 11703 |
| 2704 | 11704 |
| 2705 | 11705 |
| 2706 | 11706 |
| 2707 | 11707 |

**Unclassified shunter diesel-hydraulic 0-4-0**

| | |
|---|---|
| 2708 | 11708 |
| 2709 | 11709 |
| 2710 | 11710 |
| 2711 | 11711 |
| 2712 | 11712 |
| 2713 | 11713 |
| 2714 | 11714 |
| 2715 | 11715 |
| 2716 | 11716 |
| 2717 | 11717 |
| 2718 | 11718 |
| 2719 | 11719 |
| 2720 | |
| 2721 | |
| 2722 | |
| 2723 | |
| 2724 | |
| 2725 | |
| 2726 | |
| 2727 | |
| 2728 | |
| 2729 | |
| 2730 | |
| 2731 | |
| 2732 | |
| 2733 | |
| 2734 | |
| 2735 | |
| 2736 | |
| 2737 | |
| 2738 | |
| 2739 | |
| 2740 | |
| 2741 | |
| 2742 | |
| 2743 | |
| 2744 | |
| 2745 | |
| 2746 | |
| 2747 | |
| 2748 | |
| 2749 | |
| 2750 | |
| 2751 | |
| 2752 | |
| 2753 | |
| 2754 | |
| 2755 | |
| 2756 | |
| 2757 | |
| 2758 | |
| 2759 | |
| 2760 | |
| 2761 | |
| 2762 | |
| 2763 | |
| 2764 | |
| 2765 | |
| 2766 | |
| 2768 | |
| 2769 | |
| 2770 | |
| 2771 | |
| 2772 | |
| 2773 | |
| 2775 | |
| 2776 | |
| 2777 | |
| 2778 | |
| 2779 | |
| 2780 | |

**Unclassified shunter diesel-hydraulic 0-4-0**
2900
2901
2902
2903
2904
2905
2906
2907
2908
2909
2910
2911
2912
2913

**Unclassified shunter diesel mechanical 0-4-0**

| | |
|---|---|
| 2950 | 11500 |
| 2951 | 11501 |
| 2952 | 11502 |

**Unclassified shunter diesel-mechanical 0-4-0**

| | |
|---|---|
| 2957 | 11507 |
| 2958 | 11508 |

**Unclassified shunter diesel-electric 0-4-0**
2999

**Unclassified shunter diesel-electric 0-6-0**

| | |
|---|---|
| 3117 | 13117 |
| 3118 | 13118 |
| 3119 | 13119 |
| 3120 | 13120 |
| 3121 | 13121 |
| 3122 | 13122 |
| 3123 | 13123 |
| 3124 | 13124 |
| 3125 | 13125 |
| 3126 | 13126 |
| 3152 | 1352 |
| 3153 | 1353 |
| 3154 | 1354 |
| 3155 | 1355 |
| 3156 | 1356 |
| 3157 | 1357 |
| 3158 | 1358 |
| 3159 | 1359 |
| 3160 | 1360 |
| 3161 | 1361 |
| 3162 | 1362 |
| 3163 | 1363 |
| 3164 | 1364 |
| 3165 | 1365 |
| 3166 | 1366 |

**Unclassified shunter diesel-mechanical 0-6-0**
11104
This was the same design as a Class 04

**Unclassified shunter diesel-electric 0-6-0**
12000
12001

**Unclassified shunter diesel-electric 0-6-0**
12002

**Unclassified shunter diesel-electric 0-6-0**

| | |
|---|---|
| 12003 | 7080 |
| 12004 | 7081 |
| 12005 | 7082 |
| 12006 | 7083 |
| 12007 | 7084 |
| 12008 | 7085 |
| 12009 | 7086 |
| 12010 | 7087 |
| 12011 | 7088 |
| 12012 | 7089 |
| 12013 | 7090 |
| 12014 | 7091 |
| 12015 | 7092 |
| 12016 | 7093 |
| 12017 | 7094 |
| 12018 | 7095 |
| 12019 | 7096 |
| 12020 | 7097 |
| 12021 | 7098 |
| 12022 | 7099 |
| 12023 | 7110 |
| 12024 | 7111 |
| 12025 | 7112 |
| 12026 | 7113 |
| 12027 | 7114 |
| 12028 | 7115 |
| 12029 | 7116 |
| 12030 | 7117 |
| 12031 | 7118 |
| 12032 | 7119 |

**LNER Unclassified shunter diesel-electric 0-6-0**

| | |
|---|---|
| 15000 | 8000 |
| 15001 | 8001 |
| 15002 | 8002 |
| 15003 | 8003 |

**LNER Unclassified shunter diesel-electric 0-6-0**
15004

**GWR Unclassified shunter diesel-electric 0-6-0**
15100

**GWR Unclassified shunter diesel-electric 0-6-0**
15101
15102
15103
15104
15105
15106

**Unclassified shunter diesel-electric 0-6-0**
15107

**SR Unclassified shunter diesel-electric 0-6-0**
15201
15202
15203

**LMS Prototype Type 3 1,600hp diesel-electric Co-Co**
10000
10001

**Prototype 2,040hp diesel-mechanical 2-D-2**
10100

**Prototype Type 3 1,750hp diesel-electric 1Co-Co1**
10201
10202

**Prototype Type 4 2,000hp diesel-electric 1Co-Co1**
10203

**Prototype Type 1 827hp diesel-electric Bo-Bo**
10800

**Prototype 500hp diesel-mechanical 0-6-0**
11001

**Prototype 500hp diesel-electric 0-6-0**
D226 D0226

**Prototype 500hp diesel-hydraulic 0-6-0**
D227 D0227

**Prototype Type 4 diesel-electric Co-Co**
*DELTIC*

**Prototype Type 4 diesel-electric Co-Co**
DP2

**Prototype Type 4 diesel-electric Co-Co**
0260

**Prototype Type 5 diesel-electric Co-Co**
HS4000

**Various trial locos**

D9998
JANUS
TAURUS
VULCAN

**Unclassified electric Bo-Bo**

| | |
|---|---|
| 26500 | 6480 |
| 26501 | 6481 |

**Unclassified electric Bo-Bo**

| | |
|---|---|
| 26502 | 6490 |
| 26503 | 6491 |
| 26504 | 6492 |
| 26505 | 6493 |
| 26506 | 6494 |
| 26507 | 6495 |
| 26508 | 6496 |
| 26509 | 6497 |
| 26510 | 6498 |
| 26511 | 6499 |

**Unclassified electric Bo-Bo**

| | |
|---|---|
| 26600 | 6999 |

**Unclassified gas turbine A1A-A1A**

| | | |
|---|---|---|
| E1000 | E2000 | 18100 |

**Unclassified gas turbine 4-6-0**

GT3

**Class 01 shunter diesel-mechanical 0-4-0**

| | | |
|---|---|---|
| 01001 | 2954 | 11504 |
| 01002 | 2955 | 11505 |
| | 2956 | |

Two locos were numbered D2956, this one and the Class 01 which is preserved

**Class 02 shunter diesel-hydraulic 0-4-0**

| | |
|---|---|
| | 2850 |
| 02001 | 2851 |
| | 2852 |
| | 2855 |
| 02004 | 2856 |
| | 2857 |
| | 2859 |
| | 2861 |
| | 2862 |
| | 2863 |
| | 2864 |
| | 2865 |
| | 2869 |

**Class 03 shunter diesel-mechanical 0-6-0**

| | |
|---|---|
| | 2000 |
| | 2001 |
| | 2002 |
| | 2003 |
| 03004 | 2004 |
| 03005 | 2005 |
| | 2006 |
| 03007 | 2007 |
| 03008 | 2008 |
| 03009 | 2009 |
| 03010 | 2010 |
| | 2011 |
| 03012 | 2012 |
| 03013 | 2013 |
| 03014 | 2014 |
| | 2015 |
| 03016 | 2016 |
| 03017 | 2017 |
| | 2019 |
| 03021 | 2021 |
| 03025 | 2025 |
| 03026 | 2026 |
| | 2028 |
| 03029 | 2029 |
| | 2030 |
| | 2031 |
| | 2032 |
| | 2033 |
| 03034 | 2034 |
| 03035 | 2035 |
| | 2036 |
| | 2038 |
| | 2039 |
| | 2040 |
| | 2042 |
| | 2043 |
| 03044 | 2044 |
| 03045 | 2045 |
| 03047 | 2047 |
| | 2048 |
| | 2049 |
| 03050 | 2050 |
| | 2052 |
| | 2053 |
| | 2054 |
| 03055 | 2055 |
| 03056 | 2056 |
| | 2057 |
| 03058 | 2058 |
| 03060 | 2060 |
| 03061 | 2061 |
| 03064 | 2064 |
| | 2065 |
| 03067 | 2067 |
| 03068 | 2068 |
| | 2070 |
| | 2071 |
| | 2074 |
| 03075 | 2075 |
| 03076 | 2076 |
| | 2077 |
| 03080 | 2080 |
| | 2082 |
| | 2083 |
| | 2085 |
| 03086 | 2086 |
| | 2087 |
| | 2088 |
| 03091 | 2091 |
| 03092 | 2092 |
| | 2093 |
| 03095 | 2095 |
| 03096 | 2096 |
| 03097 | 2097 |
| 03098 | 2098 |
| | 2100 |
| | 2101 |
| 03102 | 2102 |
| 03103 | 2103 |
| 03104 | 2104 |
| 03105 | 2105 |
| 03106 | 2106 |
| 03107 | 2107 |
| 03108 | 2108 |
| 03109 | 2109 |
| 03110 | 2110 |
| 03111 | 2111 |
| | 2114 |
| | 2115 |
| | 2116 |
| 03121 | 2121 |
| | 2122 |
| | 2123 |
| | 2124 |
| | 2125 |
| | 2126 |
| | 2127 |
| 03129 | 2129 |
| | 2130 |
| | 2131 |
| | 2132 |

| | |
|---|---|
| 03135 | 2135 |
| | 2136 |
| 03137 | 2137 |
| | 2140 |
| 03142 | 2142 |
| | 2143 |
| | 2146 |
| 03147 | 2147 |
| 03149 | 2149 |
| | 2150 |
| 03151 | 2151 |
| 03153 | 2153 |
| 03154 | 2154 |
| 03155 | 2155 |
| 03156 | 2156 |
| 03157 | 2157 |
| 03159 | 2159 |
| 03160 | 2160 |
| 03161 | 2161 |
| 03163 | 2163 |
| 03164 | 2164 |
| 03165 | 2165 |
| 03166 | 2166 |
| 03167 | 2167 |
| 03168 | 2168 |
| 03169 | 2169 |
| 03171 | 2171 |
| 03172 | 2172 |
| | 2173 |
| 03174 | 2174 |
| 03175 | 2175 |
| | 2176 |
| | 2177 |
| | 2181 |
| | 2183 |
| | 2185 |
| | 2186 |
| | 2187 |
| | 2188 |
| | 2190 |
| | 2191 |
| | 2193 |
| | 2194 |
| | 2195 |
| | 2198 |
| 03370 | 2370 |
| | 2372 |
| | 2373 |
| | 2374 |
| | 2375 |
| | 2376 |
| | 2377 |
| | 2378 |
| | 2379 |
| | 2380 |
| 03382 | 2382 |
| | 2383 |
| | 2384 |
| | 2385 |
| 03386 | 2386 |
| | 2387 |
| | 2388 |
| 03389 | 2389 |
| | 2390 |
| | 2391 |
| | 2392 |
| | 2393 |
| | 2394 |
| | 2395 |
| | 2396 |
| 03397 | 2397 |
| | 2398 |

**Class 04 shunter diesel-mechanical 0-6-0**

| | |
|---|---|
| 2200 | 11100 |
| 2201 | 11101 |
| 2202 | 11102 |
| 2204 | 11105 |
| 2206 | 11107 |
| 2208 | 11109 |
| 2209 | 11110 |
| 2210 | 11111 |
| 2211 | 11112 |
| 2212 | 11113 |
| 2213 | 11114 |
| 2214 | 11115 |
| 2215 | 11121 |
| 2216 | 11122 |
| 2217 | 11123 |
| 2218 | 11124 |
| 2219 | 11125 |
| 2220 | 11126 |
| 2221 | 11127 |
| 2222 | 11128 |
| 2223 | 11129 |
| 2224 | 11130 |
| 2225 | 11131 |
| 2226 | 11132 |
| 2227 | 11133 |
| 2228 | 11134 |
| 2230 | 11149 |
| 2231 | 11150 |
| 2232 | 11151 |
| 2233 | 11152 |
| 2234 | 11153 |
| 2235 | 11154 |
| 2236 | 11155 |
| 2237 | 11156 |
| 2238 | 11157 |
| 2239 | 11158 |
| 2240 | 11159 |
| 2241 | 11160 |
| 2242 | 11212 |
| 2243 | 11213 |
| 2244 | 11214 |
| 2247 | 11217 |
| 2248 | 11218 |
| 2249 | 11219 |
| 2250 | 11220 |
| 2251 | 11221 |
| 2252 | 11222 |
| 2253 | 11223 |
| 2254 | 11224 |
| 2255 | 11225 |
| 2256 | 11226 |
| 2257 | 11227 |
| 2258 | 11228 |
| 2259 | 11229 |
| 2260 | |
| 2261 | |
| 2262 | |
| 2263 | |
| 2264 | |
| 2265 | |
| 2266 | |
| 2267 | |
| 2268 | |
| 2269 | |
| 2270 | |
| 2273 | |
| 2274 | |
| 2275 | |
| 2276 | |
| 2277 | |
| 2278 | |
| 2281 | |
| 2282 | |
| 2283 | |
| 2285 | |
| 2286 | |
| 2287 | |
| 2288 | |

**Class 04 shunter diesel-mechanical 0-6-0 (Continued...)**

| | |
|---|---|
| 2290 | |
| 2291 | |
| 2292 | |
| 2293 | |
| 2294 | |
| 2295 | |
| 2296 | |
| 2297 | |
| 2298 | |
| 2299 | |
| 2300 | |
| 2301 | |
| 2303 | |
| 2304 | |
| 2305 | |
| 2306 | |
| 2307 | |
| 2308 | |
| 2309 | |
| 2311 | |
| 2312 | |
| 2313 | |
| 2314 | |
| 2315 | |
| 2316 | |
| 2317 | |
| 2318 | |
| 2319 | |
| 2320 | |
| 2321 | |
| 2322 | |
| 2323 | |
| 2326 | |
| 2327 | |
| 2328 | |
| 2329 | |
| 2330 | |
| 2331 | |
| 2332 | |
| 2333 | |
| 2335 | |
| 2336 | |
| 2338 | |
| 2339 | |
| 2340 | |
| 2341 | S1173 |

**Class 05 shunter diesel-mechanical 0-6-0**

| | |
|---|---|
| 2550 | 11136 |
| 2551 | 11137 |
| 2552 | 11138 |
| 2553 | 11139 |
| 2555 | 11141 |
| 2556 | 11142 |
| 2557 | 11143 |
| 2558 | 11161 |
| 2559 | 11162 |
| 2560 | 11163 |
| 2561 | 11164 |
| 2562 | 11165 |
| 2563 | 11166 |
| 2564 | 11167 |
| 2565 | 11168 |
| 2566 | 11169 |
| 2567 | 11170 |
| 2568 | 11171 |
| 2569 | 11172 |
| 2570 | 11173 |
| 2571 | 11174 |
| 2572 | 11175 |
| 2573 | 11176 |
| 2574 | |
| 2575 | |
| 2576 | |
| 2577 | |
| 2579 | |
| 2580 | |
| 2581 | |
| 2582 | |
| 2583 | |
| 2584 | |
| 2585 | |
| 2586 | |
| 2588 | |
| 2589 | |
| 2590 | |
| 2591 | |
| 2592 | |
| 2593 | |
| 2594 | |
| 2596 | |
| 2597 | |
| 2598 | |
| 2599 | |
| 2600 | |
| 2601 | |
| 2602 | |
| 2603 | |
| 2604 | |
| 2605 | |
| 2606 | |
| 2607 | |
| 2608 | |
| 2609 | |
| 2610 | |
| 2611 | |
| 2612 | |
| 2613 | |
| 2614 | |
| 2615 | |
| 2616 | |
| 2617 | |
| 2618 | |

**Class 06 shunter diesel-mechanical 0-4-0**

| | |
|---|---|
| | 2410 |
| | 2411 |
| | 2412 |
| 06001 | 2413 |
| 06002 | 2414 |
| | 2415 |
| | 2416 |
| | 2417 |
| | 2418 |
| | 2419 |
| 06004 | 2421 |
| 06005 | 2422 |
| 06006 | 2423 |
| | 2424 |
| | 2425 |
| 06007 | 2426 |
| | 2427 |
| | 2428 |
| | 2429 |
| | 2430 |
| | 2431 |
| | 2432 |
| | 2433 |
| | 2434 |
| | 2435 |
| | 2436 |
| 06008 | 2437 |
| | 2438 |
| | 2439 |
| 06009 | 2440 |
| | 2441 |
| | 2442 |
| | 2443 |
| 06010 | 2444 |

**Class 07 shunter diesel-electric 0-6-0**

| | |
|---|---|
| 07002 | 2986 |
| 07003 | 2987 |
| | 2988 |
| 07006 | 2990 |
| | 2992 |
| 07009 | 2993 |
| | 2998 |

**Class 08 shunter diesel-electric 0-6-0**

| | | | |
|---|---|---|---|
| | 3001 | 13001 | |
| | 3003 | 13003 | |
| 08001 | 3004 | 13004 | |
| 08002 | 3005 | 13005 | |
| ADB966507 | 3006 | 13006 | |
| 08003 | 3007 | 13007 | |
| 08004 | 3008 | 13008 | |
| 08005 | 3009 | 13009 | |
| 08006 | 3010 | 13010 | |
| | 3011 | 13011 | |
| | 3012 | 13012 | |
| | 3013 | 13013 | |
| 08008 | 3015 | 13015 | |
| 08009 | 3016 | 13016 | |
| 08010 | 3017 | 13017 | |
| | 3020 | 13020 | |
| 08014 | 3021 | 13021 | |
| | 3024 | 13024 | |
| 08018 | 3025 | 13025 | |
| | 3026 | 13026 | |
| 08019 | 3027 | 13027 | |
| | 3028 | 13028 | |
| 08023 | 3031 | 13031 | |
| 08024 | 3032 | 13032 | |
| 08025 | 3033 | 13033 | |
| | 3034 | 13034 | |
| ADB966508 | 3035 | 13035 | |
| 08026 | 3036 | 13036 | |
| ADB966510 | 3037 | 13037 | |
| | 3038 | 13038 | |
| 08027 | 3039 | 13039 | |
| 08028 | 3040 | 13040 | |
| 08029 | 3041 | 13041 | |
| 08030 | 3042 | 13042 | |
| 08031 | 3043 | 13043 | |
| | 3045 | 13045 | |
| 08033 | 3046 | 13046 | |
| 08035 | 3048 | 13048 | |
| 08036 | 3049 | 13049 | |
| 08037 | 3050 | 13050 | |
| | 3051 | 13051 | |
| | 3052 | 13052 | |
| | 3053 | 13053 | |
| 08041 | 3054 | 13054 | |
| 08042 | 3055 | 13055 | |
| 08043 | 3056 | 13056 | |
| 08044 | 3057 | 13057 | |
| 08045 | 3058 | 13058 | |
| 08047 | 3060 | 13060 | |
| 08048 | 3061 | 13061 | |
| 08049 | 3062 | 13062 | |
| 08050 | 3063 | 13063 | |
| 08051 | 3064 | 13064 | |
| 08052 | 3065 | 13065 | |
| 08053 | 3066 | 13066 | |
| 08055 | 3068 | 13068 | |
| ADB966509 | 3069 | 13069 | |
| 08056 | 3070 | 13070 | |
| 08057 | 3071 | 13071 | |
| 08058 | 3072 | 13072 | |
| 08059 | 3073 | 13073 | |
| 08061 | 3075 | 13075 | |
| 08062 | 3076 | 13076 | |
| 08063 | 3077 | 13077 | |
| ADB966506 | 3078 | 13078 | |
| 08065 | 3080 | 13080 | |
| 08066 | 3081 | 13081 | |
| 08067 | 3082 | 13082 | |
| 08068 | 3083 | 13083 | |
| 08069 | 3084 | 13084 | |
| 08070 | 3085 | 13085 | |
| 08071 | 3086 | 13086 | |
| | 3087 | 13087 | |
| | 3088 | 13088 | |
| 08074 | 3089 | 13089 | |
| 08075 | 3090 | 13090 | |
| 08076 | 3091 | 13091 | |
| | 3093 | 13093 | |
| | 3094 | 13094 | |
| | 3095 | 13095 | |
| | 3096 | 13096 | |
| | 3097 | 13097 | |
| | 3098 | 13098 | |
| | 3099 | 13099 | |
| | 3100 | 13100 | |
| 08077 | 3102 | 13102 | |
| 08078 | 3103 | 13103 | |
| 08079 | 3104 | 13104 | |
| 08080 | 3105 | 13105 | |
| 08081 | 3106 | 13106 | |
| 08082 | 3107 | 13107 | |
| 08083 | 3108 | 13108 | |
| 08084 | 3109 | 13109 | |
| 08085 | 3110 | 13110 | |
| 08086 | 3111 | 13111 | |
| 08087 | 3112 | 13112 | |
| 08088 | 3113 | 13113 | |
| 08089 | 3114 | 13114 | |
| 08090 | 3115 | 13115 | |
| 08091 | 3116 | 13116 | |
| 08092 | 3127 | 13127 | |
| 08093 | 3128 | 13128 | |
| 08094 | 3129 | 13129 | |
| 08095 | 3130 | 13130 | |
| 08096 | 3131 | 13131 | |
| 08097 | 3132 | 13132 | |
| 08098 | 3133 | 13133 | |
| 08099 | 3134 | 13134 | |
| 08100 | 3135 | 13135 | |
| 08101 | 3136 | 13136 | |
| 08103 | 3168 | 13168 | |
| 08104 | 3169 | 13169 | |
| 08105 | 3170 | 13170 | |
| 08106 | 3171 | 13171 | |
| | 3172 | 13172 | |
| 08107 | 3173 | 13173 | |
| 08109 | 3175 | 13175 | |
| 08110 | 3176 | 13176 | |
| 08111 | 3177 | 13177 | ADB966512 |
| 08112 | 3178 | 13178 | |
| 08113 | 3179 | 13179 | |
| 08115 | 3181 | 13181 | |
| 08116 | 3182 | 13182 | |
| | 3183 | 13183 | |
| 08117 | 3184 | 13184 | ADB966513 |
| 08118 | 3185 | 13185 | |
| 08119 | 3186 | 13186 | ADB966511 |
| 08120 | 3187 | 13187 | |
| 08121 | 3188 | 13188 | |
| 08122 | 3189 | 13189 | |
| 08124 | 3191 | 13191 | |
| 08125 | 3192 | 13192 | |
| | 3193 | 13193 | |
| 08126 | 3194 | 13194 | |
| 08127 | 3195 | 13195 | |
| 08128 | 3196 | 13196 | |
| 08129 | 3197 | 13197 | |
| 08130 | 3198 | 13198 | |
| 08131 | 3199 | 13199 | |
| 08132 | 3200 | 13200 | |
| 08134 | 3202 | 13202 | |
| 08135 | 3203 | 13203 | |

**Class 08 shunter diesel-electric 0-6-0 (Continued...)**

| | | |
|---|---|---|
| 08136 | 3204 | 13204 |
| 08137 | 3205 | 13205 |
| 08138 | 3206 | 13206 |
| 08139 | 3207 | 13207 |
| 08140 | 3208 | 13208 |
| 08141 | 3209 | 13209 |
| 08142 | 3210 | 13210 |
| 08143 | 3211 | 13211 |
| 08144 | 3212 | 13212 |
| 08145 | 3213 | 13213 |
| 08146 | 3214 | 13214 |
| 08147 | 3215 | 13215 |
| 08148 | 3216 | 13216 |
| 08149 | 3217 | 13217 |
| 08150 | 3218 | 13218 |
| 08151 | 3219 | 13219 |
| 08152 | 3220 | 13220 |
| 08153 | 3221 | 13221 |
| 08154 | 3222 | 13222 |
| 08155 | 3223 | 13223 |
| 08156 | 3224 | 13224 |
| 08157 | 3225 | 13225 |
| 08158 | 3226 | 13226 |
| 08159 | 3227 | 13227 |
| 08160 | 3228 | 13228 |
| 08161 | 3229 | 13229 |
| 08162 | 3230 | 13230 |
| 08163 | 3231 | 13231 |
| 08165 | 3233 | 13233 |
| 08166 | 3234 | 13234 |
| 08167 | 3235 | 13235 |
| 08169 | 3237 | 13237 |
| 08170 | 3238 | 13238 |
| 08171 | 3239 | 13239 |
| 08172 | 3240 | 13240 |
| 08173 | 3241 | 13241 |
| 08174 | 3242 | 13242 |
| 08175 | 3243 | 13243 |
| 08176 | 3244 | 13244 |
| 08177 | 3245 | 13245 |
| 08178 | 3246 | 13246 |
| 08179 | 3247 | 13247 |
| 08180 | 3248 | 13248 |
| 08181 | 3249 | 13249 |
| 08182 | 3250 | 13250 |
| 08183 | 3251 | 13251 |
| 08184 | 3252 | 13252 |
| 08185 | 3253 | 13253 |
| 08186 | 3254 | 13254 |
| 08187 | 3256 | 13256 |
| 08188 | 3257 | 13257 |
| 08189 | 3258 | 13258 |
| 08190 | 3259 | 13259 |
| 08191 | 3260 | 13260 |
| 08192 | 3262 | 13262 |
| 08193 | 3263 | 13263 |
| 08194 | 3264 | 13264 |
| 08196 | 3266 | 13266 |
| 08197 | 3267 | 13267 |
| 08198 | 3268 | 13268 |
| 08199 | 3269 | 13269 |
| 08200 | 3270 | 13270 |
| 08201 | 3271 | 13271 |
| 08204 | 3274 | 13274 |
| 08205 | 3275 | 13275 |
| 08206 | 3276 | 13276 |
| 08207 | 3277 | 13277 |
| 08208 | 3278 | 13278 |
| 08209 | 3279 | 13279 |
| 08210 | 3280 | 13280 |
| 08211 | 3281 | 13281 |
| 08212 | 3282 | 13282 |
| 08213 | 3283 | 13283 |
| 08214 | 3284 | 13284 |
| 08215 | 3285 | 13285 |

| | | | |
|---|---|---|---|
| 08216 | 3286 | 13286 | |
| 08217 | 3287 | 13287 | |
| 08218 | 3288 | 13288 | |
| 08219 | 3289 | 13289 | |
| 08221 | 3291 | 13291 | |
| 08222 | 3292 | 13292 | |
| 08223 | 3293 | 13293 | |
| 08224 | 3294 | 13294 | |
| 08225 | 3295 | 13295 | |
| 08226 | 3296 | 13296 | |
| 08227 | 3297 | 13297 | |
| 08228 | 3298 | 13298 | |
| 08229 | 3299 | 13299 | |
| 08230 | 3300 | 13300 | |
| 08231 | 3301 | 13301 | |
| 08232 | 3302 | 13302 | |
| 08233 | 3303 | 13303 | |
| 08234 | 3304 | 13304 | |
| 08235 | 3305 | 13305 | |
| 08236 | 3306 | 13306 | |
| 08237 | 3307 | 13307 | |
| 08239 | 3309 | 13309 | |
| 08240 | 3310 | 13310 | |
| 08241 | 3311 | 13311 | |
| 08242 | 3312 | 13312 | |
| 08243 | 3313 | 13313 | |
| 08244 | 3314 | 13314 | |
| 08245 | 3315 | 13315 | |
| 08246 | 3316 | 13316 | |
| 08247 | 3317 | 13317 | |
| 08248 | 3318 | 13318 | |
| 08249 | 3319 | 13319 | |
| 08250 | 3320 | 13320 | |
| 08251 | 3321 | 13321 | |
| 08252 | 3322 | 13322 | |
| 08253 | 3323 | 13323 | |
| 08254 | 3324 | 13324 | |
| 08255 | 3325 | 13325 | |
| 08256 | 3326 | 13326 | |
| 08257 | 3327 | 13327 | |
| 08258 | 3328 | 13328 | |
| 08260 | 3330 | 13330 | |
| 08261 | 3331 | 13331 | |
| 08262 | 3332 | 13332 | |
| 08263 | 3333 | 13333 | |
| 08264 | 3334 | 13334 | |
| 08265 | 3335 | 13335 | |
| 08267 | 97801 | 3337 | 13337 |
| 08268 | 3338 | 13338 | |
| 08269 | 3339 | 13339 | |
| 08270 | 3340 | 13340 | |
| 08271 | 3341 | 13341 | |
| 08272 | 3342 | 13342 | |
| 08273 | 3343 | 13343 | |
| 08274 | 3344 | 13344 | |
| 08275 | 3345 | 13345 | |
| 08276 | 3346 | 13346 | |
| 08277 | 3347 | 13347 | |
| 08278 | 3348 | 13348 | |
| 08279 | 3349 | 13349 | |
| 08280 | 3350 | 13350 | |
| 08281 | 3351 | 13351 | |
| 08282 | 3352 | 13352 | |
| 08283 | 3353 | 13353 | |
| 08284 | 3354 | 13354 | |
| 08285 | 3355 | 13355 | |
| 08286 | 3356 | 13356 | |
| 08287 | 3357 | 13357 | |
| 08289 | 3359 | | |
| 08290 | 3360 | | |
| 08291 | 3361 | | |
| 08292 | 3362 | 13362 | |
| 08293 | 3363 | 13363 | |
| 08294 | 3364 | 13364 | |
| 08295 | 3365 | 13365 | |
| 08296 | 3366 | 13366 | |

| | |
|---|---|
| 08297 | 3367 |
| 08298 | 3368 |
| 08299 | 3369 |
| 08300 | 3370 |
| 08301 | 3371 |
| 08302 | 3372 |
| 08303 | 3373 |
| 08304 | 3374 |
| 08305 | 3375 |
| 08306 | 3376 |
| 08307 | 3377 |
| 08309 | 3379 |
| 08310 | 3380 |
| 08311 | 3381 |
| 08312 | 3382 |
| 08313 | 3383 |
| 08314 | 3384 |
| 08315 | 3385 |
| 08316 | 3386 |
| 08317 | 3387 |
| 08318 | 3388 |
| 08319 | 3389 |
| 08320 | 3390 |
| 08321 | 3391 |
| 08322 | 3392 |
| 08323 | 3393 |
| 08324 | 3394 |
| 08325 | 3395 |
| 08326 | 3396 |
| 08327 | 3397 |
| 08328 | 3398 |
| 08329 | 3399 |
| 08330 | 3400 |
| 08332 | 3402 |
| 08333 | 3403 |
| 08334 | 3404 |
| 08335 | 3405 |
| 08336 | 3406 |
| 08337 | 3407 |
| 08338 | 3408 |
| 08339 | 3409 |
| 08340 | 3410 |
| 08341 | 3411 |
| 08342 | 3412 |
| 08343 | 3413 |
| 08344 | 3414 |
| 08345 | 3415 |
| 08346 | 3416 |
| 08347 | 3417 |
| 08348 | 3418 |
| 08349 | 3419 |
| 08350 | 3420 |
| 08351 | 3421 |
| 08352 | 3422 |
| 08353 | 3423 |
| 08354 | 3424 |
| 08355 | 3425 |
| 08356 | 3426 |
| 08357 | 3427 |
| 08358 | 3428 |
| 08360 | 3430 |
| 08361 | 3431 |
| 08362 | 3432 |
| 08363 | 3433 |
| 08364 | 3434 |
| 08365 | 3435 |
| 08366 | 3436 |
| 08367 | 3437 |
| 08368 | 3438 |
| 08369 | 3454 |
| 08370 | 3455 |
| 08371 | 3456 |
| 08372 | 3457 |
| 08373 | 3458 |
| 08374 | 3459 |
| 08376 | 3461 |
| 08378 | 3463 |
| 08379 | 3464 |
| 08380 | 3465 |
| 08381 | 3466 |
| 08382 | 3467 |
| 08383 | 3468 |
| 08384 | 3469 |
| 08385 | 3470 |
| 08386 | 3471 |
| 08387 | 3472 |
| 08388 | 3503 |
| 08390 | 3505 |
| 08391 | 3506 |
| 08392 | 3507 |
| 08393 | 3508 |
| 08394 | 3509 |
| 08395 | 3510 |
| 08396 | 3511 |
| 08397 | 3512 |
| 08398 | 3513 |
| 08399 | 3514 |
| 08400 | 3515 |
| 08402 | 3517 |
| 08403 | 3518 |
| 08404 | 3519 |
| 08406 | 3521 |
| 08407 | 3522 |
| 08408 | 3523 |
| 08409 | 3524 |
| 08412 | 3527 |
| 08413 | 3528 |
| 08414 | 3529 |
| 08415 | 3530 |
| 08416 | 3531 |
| 08419 | 3534 |
| 08420 | 3535 |
| 08422 | 3537 |
| 08424 | 3539 |
| 08425 | 3540 |
| 08426 | 3541 |
| 08427 | 3542 |
| 08429 | 3544 |
| 08430 | 3545 |
| 08431 | 3546 |
| 08432 | 3547 |
| 08433 | 3548 |
| 08434 | 3549 |
| 08435 | 3550 |
| 08437 | 3552 |
| 08438 | 3553 |
| 08439 | 3554 |
| 08440 | 3555 |
| 08446 | 3561 |
| 08448 | 3563 |
| 08449 | 3564 |
| 08450 | 3565 |
| 08452 | 3567 |
| 08453 | 3568 |
| 08455 | 3570 |
| 08456 | 3571 |
| 08457 | 3572 |
| 08458 | 3573 |
| 08459 | 3574 |
| 08461 | 3576 |
| 08463 | 3578 |
| 08464 | 3579 |
| 08465 | 3580 |
| 08466 | 3581 |
| 08467 | 3582 |
| 08468 | 3583 |
| 08469 | 3584 |
| 08470 | 3585 |
| 08474 | 3589 |
| 08475 | 3590 |
| 08477 | 3592 |
| 08478 | 3593 |

**Class 08 shunter diesel-electric 0-6-0 (Continued...)**

| | |
|---|---|
| 08481 | 3596 |
| 08482 | 3597 |
| 08486 | 3601 |
| 08487 | 3602 |
| 08488 | 3603 |
| 08489 | 3604 |
| 08491 | 3606 |
| 08492 | 3607 |
| 08493 | 3608 |
| 08494 | 3609 |
| 08496 | 3611 |
| 08497 | 3652 |
| 08498 | 3653 |
| 08501 | 3656 |
| 08504 | 3659 |
| 08505 | 3660 |
| 08506 | 3661 |
| 08508 | 3663 |
| 08509 | 3664 |
| 08510 | 3672 |
| 08512 | 3674 |
| 08513 | 3675 |
| 08514 | 3676 |
| 08515 | 3677 |
| 08517 | 3679 |
| 08518 | 3680 |
| 08519 | 3681 |
| 08520 | 3682 |
| 08521 | 3683 |
| 08522 | 3684 |
| 08524 | 3686 |
| 08526 | 3688 |
| 08529 | 3691 |
| 08532 | 3694 |
| 08533 | 3695 |
| 08534 | 3696 |
| 08535 | 3699 |
| 08537 | 3701 |
| 08538 | 3702 |
| 08539 | 3703 |
| 08540 | 3704 |
| 08541 | 3705 |
| 08542 | 3706 |
| 08543 | 3707 |
| 08544 | 3708 |
| 08545 | 3709 |
| 08546 | 3710 |
| 08547 | 3711 |
| 08548 | 3712 |
| 08549 | 3713 |
| 08550 | 3714 |
| 08551 | 3715 |
| 08552 | 3716 |
| 08553 | 3717 |
| 08554 | 3718 |
| 08555 | 3722 |
| 08557 | 3724 |
| 08558 | 3725 |
| 08559 | 3726 |
| 08560 | 3727 |
| 08561 | 3728 |
| 08562 | 3729 |
| 08563 | 3730 |
| 08564 | 3731 |
| 08565 | 3732 |
| 08566 | 3733 |
| 08569 | 3736 |
| 08570 | 3737 |
| 08572 | 3739 |
| 08574 | 3741 |
| 08576 | 3743 |
| 08577 | 3744 |
| 08579 | 3746 |
| 08581 | 3748 |
| 08582 | 3749 |
| 08583 | 3750 |
| 08584 | 3751 |
| 08586 | 3753 |
| 08587 | 3754 |
| 08589 | 3756 |
| 08591 | 3758 |
| 08594 | 3761 |
| 08595 | 3762 |
| 08597 | 3764 |
| 08599 | 3766 |
| 08601 | 3768 |
| 08603 | 3770 |
| 08606 | 3773 |
| 08607 | 3774 |
| 08608 | 3775 |
| 08609 | 3776 |
| 08610 | 3777 |
| 08612 | 3779 |
| 08614 | 3781 |
| 08618 | 3785 |
| 08619 | 3786 |
| 08621 | 3788 |
| 08625 | 3792 |
| 08626 | 3793 |
| 08627 | 3794 |
| 08628 | 3795 |
| 08634 | 3801 |
| 08636 | 3803 |
| 08637 | 3805 |
| 08638 | 3805 |
| 08639 | 3806 |
| 08640 | 3807 |
| 08642 | 3809 |
| 08646 | 3813 |
| 08647 | 3814 |
| 08651 | 3818 |
| 08654 | 3821 |
| 08655 | 3822 |
| 08656 | 3823 |
| 08657 | 3824 |
| 08658 | 3825 |
| 08659 | 3826 |
| 08660 | 3827 |
| 08661 | 3828 |
| 08662 | 3829 |
| 08664 | 3831 |
| 08665 | 3832 |
| 08666 | 3833 |
| 08667 | 3834 |
| 08668 | 3835 |
| 08671 | 3838 |
| 08672 | 3839 |
| 08673 | 3840 |
| 08674 | 3841 |
| 08675 | 3842 |
| 08677 | 3844 |
| 08679 | 3846 |
| 08680 | 3847 |
| 08681 | 3848 |
| 08684 | 3851 |
| 08686 | 3853 |
| 08688 | 3855 |
| 08689 | 3856 |
| 08692 | 3859 |
| 08693 | 3860 |
| 08695 | 3862 |
| 08697 | 3864 |
| 08698 | 3865 |
| 08702 | 3869 |
| 08705 | 3872 |
| 08707 | 3874 |
| 08708 | 3875 |
| 08710 | 3877 |
| 08712 | 3879 |
| 08713 | 3880 |
| 08715 | 3882 |

| | | |
|---|---|---|
| 08716 | 3883 | |
| | 3885 | |
| 08718 | 3886 | |
| 08719 | 3887 | |
| 08720 | 3888 | |
| 08722 | 3890 | |
| 08723 | 3891 | |
| 08725 | 3893 | |
| 08726 | 3894 | |
| 08727 | 3895 | |
| 08728 | 3896 | |
| 08729 | 3897 | |
| 08731 | 3899 | |
| 08733 | 3901 | |
| 08734 | 3902 | |
| 08736 | 3904 | |
| 08739 | 3907 | |
| 08740 | 3908 | |
| 08741 | 3909 | |
| 08744 | 3912 | |
| 08745 | 3913 | |
| 08746 | 3914 | |
| 08747 | 3915 | |
| 08748 | 3916 | |
| 08751 | 3919 | |
| 08753 | 3921 | |
| 08755 | 3923 | |
| 08758 | 3926 | |
| 08760 | 3928 | |
| 08761 | 3929 | |
| 08763 | 3931 | |
| 08768 | 3936 | |
| 08770 | 3938 | |
| 08771 | 3939 | |
| 08775 | 3943 | |
| 08776 | 3944 | |
| 08777 | 3945 | |
| 08778 | 3946 | |
| 08779 | 3947 | |
| 08789 | 3957 | |
| 08791 | 3959 | |
| 08792 | 3960 | |
| 08793 | 3961 | |
| 08794 | 3962 | |
| 08796 | 3964 | |
| 08797 | 3965 | |
| 08800 | 3968 | |
| 08801 | 3969 | |
| 08803 | 3971 | |
| 08806 | 3974 | |
| 08807 | 3975 | |
| 08808 | 3976 | |
| 08811 | 3979 | |
| 08812 | 3980 | |
| 08813 | 3981 | |
| 08814 | 3982 | |
| 08815 | 3983 | |
| 08816 | 3984 | |
| 08817 | 3985 | |
| 08819 | 3987 | |
| 08820 | 3988 | |
| 08821 | 3989 | |
| 08826 | 3994 | |
| 08827 | 3995 | |
| 08828 | 3996 | |
| 08829 | 3997 | |
| 08831 | 3999 | |
| 08837 | 4005 | |
| 08838 | 4006 | |
| 08839 | 4007 | |
| 08840 | 4008 | |
| 08841 | 4009 | |
| 08842 | 4010 | |
| 08843 | 4011 | |
| 08844 | 4012 | |
| 08848 | 4016 | |
| 08849 | 4017 | |
| 08851 | 4019 | |
| 08852 | 4020 | |
| 08854 | 4022 | |
| 08855 | 4023 | |
| 08856 | 4024 | |
| 08857 | 4025 | |
| 08858 | 4026 | |
| 08859 | 4027 | |
| 08860 | 4028 | |
| 08861 | 4029 | |
| 08862 | 4030 | |
| 08863 | 4031 | |
| 08864 | 4032 | |
| 08866 | 4034 | |
| 08867 | 4035 | |
| 08869 | 4037 | |
| 08875 | 4043 | |
| 08876 | 4044 | |
| 08878 | 4046 | |
| 08880 | 4048 | |
| 08882 | 4096 | |
| 08883 | 4097 | |
| 08884 | 4098 | |
| 08886 | 4116 | |
| 08889 | 4119 | |
| 08890 | 4120 | |
| 08893 | 4123 | |
| 08894 | 4124 | |
| 08895 | 4125 | |
| 08897 | 4127 | |
| 08898 | 4128 | |
| 08900 | 4130 | |
| 08901 | 4131 | |
| 08902 | 4132 | |
| 08906 | 4136 | |
| 08909 | 4139 | |
| 08910 | 4140 | |
| 08914 | 4144 | |
| 08916 | 4146 | |
| 08917 | 4147 | |
| 08919 | 4149 | |
| 08920 | 4150 | |
| 08923 | 4153 | |
| 08926 | 4156 | |
| 08928 | 4158 | |
| 08929 | 4159 | |
| 08930 | 4160 | |
| 08931 | 4161 | |
| 08932 | 4162 | |
| 08935 | 4165 | |
| 08938 | 4168 | |
| 08940 | 4170 | |
| 08941 | 4171 | |
| 08942 | 4172 | |
| 08945 | 4175 | |
| 08946 | 4176 | |
| 08949 | 4179 | |
| 08951 | 4181 | |
| 08952 | 4182 | |
| 08953 | 4183 | |
| 08955 | 4185 | |
| 08957 | 4191 | |
| 08958 | 4192 | |
| 08991 | 3273 | 08203 |
| 08992 | 3329 | 08259 |

**Class 09 shunter diesel-electric 0-6-0**

| | | |
|---|---|---|
| 09003 | 3667 | |
| 09005 | 3669 | |
| 09008 | 3719 | |
| 09011 | 4099 | |
| 09013 | 4101 | |
| 09016 | 97806 | 4104 |
| 09020 | 4108 | |
| 09021 | 4109 | |

**Class 09 shunter diesel-electric 0-6-0 (Continued...)**

| 09101 | 08833 | 4001 |
|---|---|---|
| 09102 | 08832 | 4000 |
| 09103 | 08766 | 3934 |
| 09104 | 08749 | 3917 |
| 09105 | 08835 | 4003 |
| 09202 | 08732 | 3900 |
| 09203 | 08781 | 3949 |
| 09205 | 08620 | 3787 |

**Class 10 shunter diesel-electric 0-6-0**

| 3137 | 13137 |
|---|---|
| 3138 | 13138 |
| 3139 | 13139 |
| 3140 | 13140 |
| 3141 | 13141 |
| 3142 | 13142 |
| 3143 | 13143 |
| 3144 | 13144 |
| 3145 | 13145 |
| 3146 | 13146 |
| 3147 | 13147 |
| 3148 | 13148 |
| 3149 | 13149 |
| 3150 | 13150 |
| 3151 | 13151 |

3439
3440
3441
3442
3443
3444
3445
3446
3447
3448
3449
3450
3451
3453
3473
3474
3475
3476
3477
3478
3479
3480
3481
3482
3483
3484
3485
3486
3487
3488
3490
3491
3492
3493
3494
3495
3496
3497
3498
3499
3500
3501
3502
3612
3613
3614
3615
3616
3617
3618
3619
3620
3621
3622
3623
3624
3625
3626
3627
3628
3629
3630
3631
3632
3633
3634
3635
3636
3637
3638
3639
3640
3641
3642
3643
3644
3645
3646
3647
3648
3649
3650
3651
4049
4050
4051
4052
4053
4054
4055
4056
4057
4058
4059
4060
4061
4062
4063
4064
4065
4066
4068
4069
4070
4071
4072
4073
4074
4075
4076
4077
4078
4079
4080
4081
4082
4083
4084
4085
4086
4087
4088
4089
4090
4091
4093
4094

**Class 11 shunter diesel-electric 0-6-0**

| | |
|---|---|
| 12033 | 7120 |
| 12034 | 7121 |
| 12035 | 7122 |
| 12036 | 7123 |
| 12037 | 7124 |
| 12038 | 7125 |
| 12039 | 7126 |
| 12040 | 7127 |
| 12041 | 7128 |
| 12042 | 7129 |
| 12043 | 7130 |
| 12044 | 7131 |

12045
12046
12047
12048
12049
12050
12051
12053
12054
12055
12056
12057
12058
12059
12060
12061
12062
12063
12064
12065
12066
12067
12068
12069
12070
12071
12072
12073
12074
12075
12076
12078
12079
12080
12081
12084
12085
12086
12087
12089
12090
12091
12092
12094
12095
12096
12097
12098
12100
12101
12102
12103
12104
12105
12106
12107
12108
12109
12110
12111
12112
12113
12114
12115
12116
12117
12118
12119
12120
12121
12122
12123
12124
12125
12126
12127
12128
12129
12130
12132
12133
12134
12135
12136
12137
12138

**Class 12 shunter diesel-electric 0-6-0**

15211
15212
15213
15214
15215
15216
15217
15218
15219
15220
15221
15222
15223
15225
15226
15227
15228
15229
15230
15231
15232
15233
15234
15235
15236

**Class 13 shunter diesel-electric 0-6-0+0-6-0**

| | |
|---|---|
| 13001 | 4501 (4189 + 4190) |
| 13002 | 4502 (4187 + 3697) |
| 13003 | 4500 (4188 + 3698) |

**Class 14 Type 1 diesel-hydraulic 0-6-0**

9501
9503
9505
9506
9507
9508
9509
9510
9511
9512
9514
9515
9517
9519
9522
9527
9528
9530
9532
9533

**Class 14 Type 1 diesel-hydraulic 0-6-0 (Continued...)**
9534
9535
9536
9538
9540
9541
9542
9543
9544
9545
9546
9547
9548
9549
9550
9552
9554

**Class 15 Type 1 diesel-electric Bo-Bo**
8200
8201
8202
8203 DB968003
8204
8205
8206
8207
8208
8209
8210
8211
8212
8213
8214
8215
8216
8217
8218
8219
8220
8221
8222
8223
8224
8225
8226
8227
8228
8229
8230
8231
8232
8234
8235
8236
8237 DB968002
8238
8239
8240
8241
8242
8243 DB968000

**Class 16 Type 1 diesel-electric Bo-Bo**
8400
8401
8402
8403
8404
8405
8406
8407
8408
8409

**Class 17 Type 1 diesel-electric Bo-Bo**
8500
8501
8502
8503
8504
8505
8506
8507
8508
8509
8510
8511
8512
8513
8514
8515
8516
8517
8518
8519
8520
8521 S18521
8522
8523
8524
8525
8526
8527
8528
8529
8530
8531
8532
8533
8534
8535
8536
8537
8538
8539
8540
8541
8542
8543
8544
8545
8546
8547
8548
8549
8550
8551
8552
8553
8554
8555
8556
8557
8558
8559
8560
8561
8562
8563
8564
8565
8566
8567
8569
8570
8571
8572
8573
8574
8575

8576
8577
8578
8579
8580
8581
8582
8583
8584
8585
8586
8587
8588
8589
8590
8591
8592
8593
8594
8595
8596
8597
8598
8599
8600
8601
8602
8603
8604
8605
8606
8607
8608
8609
8610
8611
8612
8613
8614
8615
8616

**Class 20 Type 1 diesel-electric Bo-Bo**

| | | |
|---|---|---|
| 20002 | 8002 | |
| 20003 | 8003 | |
| 20004 | 8004 | |
| 20005 | 8005 | |
| 20006 | 8006 | |
| 20008 | 8008 | |
| 20009 | 8009 | |
| 20010 | 8010 | |
| 20011 | 8011 | |
| 20012 | 8012 | |
| 20013 | 8013 | |
| 20014 | 8014 | |
| 20015 | 8015 | |
| 20017 | 8017 | |
| 20018 | 8018 | |
| 20019 | 8019 | |
| 20021 | 8021 | |
| 20022 | 8022 | |
| 20023 | 20301 | 8023 |
| 20024 | 8024 | |
| 20025 | 8025 | |
| 20026 | 8026 | |
| 20027 | 8027 | |
| 20028 | 8028 | |
| 20029 | 8029 | |
| 20030 | 8030 | |
| 20032 | 8032 | |
| 20033 | 8033 | |
| 20034 | 8034 | |
| 20036 | 8036 | |
| 20037 | 8037 | |
| 20038 | 8038 | |
| 20039 | 8039 | |
| 20040 | 8040 | |
| 20043 | 8043 | |
| 20044 | 8044 | |
| 20045 | 8045 | |
| 20046 | 8046 | |
| 20049 | 8049 | |
| 20051 | 8051 | |
| 20052 | 8052 | |
| 20053 | 8053 | |
| 20054 | 8054 | |
| 20055 | 8055 | |
| 20058 | 8058 | |
| 20061 | 8061 | |
| 20062 | 8062 | |
| 20064 | 8064 | |
| 20065 | 8065 | |
| 20067 | 8067 | |
| 20068 | 8068 | |
| 20070 | 8070 | |
| 20071 | 8071 | |
| 20072 | 8072 | |
| 20073 | 8073 | |
| 20074 | 8074 | |
| 20076 | 8076 | |
| 20077 | 8077 | |
| 20078 | 8078 | |
| 20079 | 8079 | |
| 20080 | 8080 | |
| 20082 | 8082 | |
| 20085 | 8085 | |
| 20086 | 8086 | |
| 20089 | 8089 | |
| 20090 | 8090 | |
| 20091 | 8091 | |
| 20092 | 8092 | |
| 20093 | 8093 | |
| 20094 | 8094 | |
| 20097 | 8097 | |
| 20099 | 8099 | |
| 20100 | 8100 | |
| 20103 | 8103 | |
| 20105 | 8105 | |
| 20106 | 8106 | |
| 20108 | 8108 | |
| 20109 | 8109 | |
| 20111 | 8111 | |
| 20112 | 8112 | |
| 20113 | 8113 | |
| 20114 | 8114 | |
| 20115 | 8115 | |
| 20116 | 8116 | |
| 20119 | 8119 | |
| 20122 | 8122 | |
| 20123 | 8123 | |
| 20124 | 8124 | |
| 20125 | 8125 | |
| 20126 | 8126 | |
| 20129 | 8129 | |
| 20130 | 8130 | |
| 20133 | 8133 | |
| 20134 | 20303 | 8134 |
| 20135 | 8135 | |
| 20136 | 8136 | |
| 20138 | 8138 | |
| 20139 | 8139 | |
| 20140 | 8140 | |
| 20141 | 8141 | |
| 20143 | 8143 | |
| 20144 | 8144 | |
| 20145 | 8145 | |
| 20146 | 8146 | |
| 20147 | 8147 | |
| 20148 | 8148 | |
| 20149 | 8149 | |
| 20150 | 8150 | |
| 20151 | 8151 | |

**Class 20 Type 1 diesel-electric Bo-Bo (Continued...)**

| | | | |
|---|---|---|---|
| 20152 | 8152 | | |
| 20153 | 8153 | | |
| 20155 | 8155 | | |
| 20156 | 8156 | | |
| 20157 | 8157 | | |
| 20158 | 8158 | | |
| 20159 | 8159 | | |
| 20160 | 8160 | | |
| 20161 | 8161 | | |
| 20162 | 8162 | | |
| 20163 | 8163 | | |
| 20164 | 8164 | | |
| 20165 | 8165 | | |
| 20167 | 8167 | | |
| 20170 | 8170 | | |
| 20171 | 8171 | | |
| 20172 | 20305 | 8172 | |
| 20173 | 20306 | 8173 | |
| 20174 | 8174 | | |
| 20175 | 8175 | | |
| 20176 | 8176 | | |
| 20177 | 8177 | | |
| 20178 | 8178 | | |
| 20179 | 8179 | | |
| 20180 | 8180 | | |
| 20181 | 8181 | | |
| 20182 | 8182 | | |
| 20183 | 8183 | | |
| 20184 | 8184 | | |
| 20185 | 8185 | | |
| 20186 | 8186 | | |
| 20191 | 8190 | | |
| 20192 | 8192 | | |
| 20193 | 8193 | | |
| 20195 | 8195 | | |
| 20196 | 20308 | 8196 | |
| 20197 | 8197 | | |
| 20198 | 8198 | | |
| 20199 | 8199 | | |
| 20200 | 8300 | | |
| 20201 | 8301 | | |
| 20202 | 8302 | | |
| 20203 | 8303 | | |
| 20204 | 8304 | | |
| 20206 | 8306 | | |
| 20207 | 8307 | | |
| 20208 | 8308 | | |
| 20209 | 8309 | | |
| 20210 | 8310 | | |
| 20211 | 8311 | | |
| 20212 | 8312 | | |
| 20213 | 8313 | | |
| 20215 | 8315 | | |
| 20216 | 8316 | | |
| 20217 | 8317 | | |
| 20218 | 8318 | | |
| 20220 | 8320 | | |
| 20221 | 8321 | | |
| 20222 | 8322 | | |
| 20223 | 8323 | | |
| 20224 | 8324 | | |
| 20226 | 8326 | | |
| 20306 | 20131 | 8131 | |
| 20307 | 20128 | 8050 | |
| 20310 | 20190 | 8190 | |
| 20313 | 20194 | 20307 | 8194 |
| 20315 | 20104 | 8104 | |
| 20902 | 20060 | 8060 | |

Note: Numbers 20301-308 were used twice

**Class 21 Type 2 diesel-electric Bo-Bo**

6104
6105
6109
6110
6111
6115
6117
6118
6120
6122
6125
6126
6127
6128
6131
6134
6135
6136
6138
6139
6140
6141
6142
6143
6144
6145
6146
6147
6148
6149
6150
6151
6152
6153
6154
6155
6156
6157

**Class 22 Type 2 diesel-hydraulic B-B**

6300
6301
6302
6303
6304
6305
6306
6307
6308
6309
6310
6311
6312
6313
6314
6315
6316
6317
6318
6319
6320
6321
6322
6323
6324
6325
6326
6327
6328
6329
6330
6331
6332
6333
6334
6335
6336
6337
6338
6339

6340
6341
6342
6343
6344
6345
6346
6347
6348
6349
6350
6351
6352
6353
6354
6355
6356
6357

**Class 23 Type 2 diesel-electric Bo-Bo**

5900
5901
5902
5903
5904
5905
5906
5907
5908
5909

---

**Class 24 Type 2 diesel-electric Bo-Bo**

| | |
|---|---|
| 24001 | 5001 |
| 24002 | 5002 |
| 24003 | 5003 |
| 24004 | 5004 |
| | 5005 |
| 24005 | 5000 |
| 24006 | 5006 |
| 24007 | 5007 |
| 24008 | 5008 |
| 24009 | 5009 |
| 24010 | 5010 |
| 24011 | 5011 |
| 24012 | 5012 |
| 24013 | 5013 |
| 24014 | 5014 |
| 24015 | 5015 |
| 24016 | 5016 |
| 24017 | 5017 |
| 24018 | 5018 |
| 24019 | 5019 |
| 24020 | 5020 |
| 24021 | 5021 |
| 24022 | 5022 |
| 24023 | 5023 |
| 24024 | 5024 |
| 24025 | 5025 |
| 24026 | 5026 |
| 24027 | 5027 |
| | 5028 |
| 24029 | 5029 |
| 24030 | 5030 |
| 24031 | 5031 |
| 24033 | 5033 |
| 24034 | 5034 |
| 24035 | 5035 |
| 24036 | 5036 |
| 24037 | 5037 |
| 24038 | 5038 |
| 24039 | 5039 |
| 24040 | 5040 |
| 24041 | 5041 |
| 24042 | 5042 |
| | 5043 |
| 24044 | 5044 |
| 24045 | 5045 |
| 24046 | 5046 |
| 24047 | 5047 |
| 24048 | 5048 |
| 24049 | 5049 |
| 24050 | 5050 |
| | 5051 |
| 24052 | 5052 |
| 24053 | 5053 |
| 24055 | 5055 |
| 24056 | 5056 |
| 24057 | 5057 |
| 24058 | 5058 |
| 24059 | 5059 |
| 24060 | 5060 |
| 24062 | 5062 |
| 24063 | 5063 |
| 24064 | 5064 |
| 24065 | 5065 |
| 24066 | 5066 |
| | 5067 |
| | 5068 |
| 24069 | 5069 |
| 24070 | 5070 |
| 24071 | 5071 |
| 24072 | 5072 |
| 24073 | 5073 |
| 24074 | 5074 |
| 24075 | 5075 |
| 24076 | 5076 |
| 24077 | 5077 |
| 24078 | 5078 |
| 24079 | 5079 |
| 24080 | 5080 |
| 24082 | 5082 |
| 24083 | 5083 |
| 24084 | 5084 |
| 24085 | 5085 |
| 24086 | 5086 |
| 24087 | 5087 |
| | 5088 |
| 24089 | 5089 |
| 24090 | 5090 |
| 24091 | 5091 |
| 24092 | 5092 |
| | 5093 |
| 24094 | 5094 |
| 24095 | 5095 |
| 24096 | 5096 |
| 24097 | 5097 |
| 24098 | 5098 |
| 24099 | 5099 |
| 24100 | 5100 |
| 24101 | 5101 |
| 24102 | 5102 |
| 24103 | 5103 |
| 24104 | 5104 |
| 24105 | 5105 |
| 24106 | 5106 |
| 24107 | 5107 |
| 24108 | 5108 |
| 24109 | 5109 |
| 24110 | 5110 |
| 24111 | 5111 |
| 24112 | 5112 |
| 24113 | 5113 |
| | 5114 |
| 24115 | 5115 |
| 24116 | 5116 |
| 24117 | 5117 |
| 24118 | 5118 |
| 24119 | 5119 |
| 24120 | 5120 |
| 24121 | 5121 |
| | 5122 |
| 24123 | 5123 |
| 24124 | 5124 |

**Class 24 Type 2 diesel-electric Bo-Bo (Continued...)**

| | | |
|---|---|---|
| 24125 | 5125 | |
| 24126 | 5126 | |
| 24127 | 5127 | |
| 24128 | 5128 | |
| 24129 | 5129 | |
| 24130 | 5130 | |
| | 5131 | |
| 24132 | 5132 | |
| 24133 | 5133 | |
| 24134 | 5134 | |
| 24135 | 5135 | |
| 24136 | 5136 | |
| 24137 | 5137 | |
| | 5138 | |
| | 5139 | |
| 24140 | 5140 | |
| 24141 | 5141 | |
| 24142 | 5142 | TDB968009 |
| 24143 | 5143 | |
| 24144 | 5144 | |
| 24145 | 5145 | |
| 24146 | 5146 | |
| 24147 | 5147 | |
| 24148 | 5148 | |
| | 5149 | |
| 24150 | 5150 | |

**Class 25 Type 2 diesel-electric Bo-Bo**

| | |
|---|---|
| 25001 | 5151 |
| 25002 | 5152 |
| 25003 | 5153 |
| 25004 | 5154 |
| 25005 | 5155 |
| 25006 | 5156 |
| 25007 | 5157 |
| 25008 | 5158 |
| 25009 | 5159 |
| 25010 | 5160 |
| 25011 | 5161 |
| 25012 | 5162 |
| 25013 | 5163 |
| 25014 | 5164 |
| 25015 | 5165 |
| 25016 | 5166 |
| 25017 | 5167 |
| 25018 | 5168 |
| 25019 | 5169 |
| 25020 | 5170 |
| 25021 | 5171 |
| 25022 | 5172 |
| 25023 | 5173 |
| 25024 | 5174 |
| 25025 | 5175 |
| 25026 | 5176 |
| 25027 | 5177 |
| 25028 | 5178 |
| 25029 | 5179 |
| 25030 | 5180 |
| 25031 | 5181 |
| 25032 | 5182 |
| 25033 | 5183 |
| 25034 | 5184 |
| 25036 | 5186 |
| 25037 | 5187 |
| 25038 | 5188 |
| 25039 | 5189 |
| 25040 | 5180 |
| 25041 | 5191 |
| 25042 | 5192 |
| 25043 | 5193 |
| 25044 | 5194 |
| 25045 | 5195 |
| 25046 | 5196 |
| 25047 | 5197 |
| 25048 | 5198 |
| 25049 | 5199 |
| 25050 | 5200 |
| 25051 | 5201 |
| 25052 | 5202 |
| 25053 | 5203 |
| 25054 | 5204 |
| 25055 | 5205 |
| 25056 | 5206 |
| 25058 | 5208 |
| 25060 | 5210 |
| 25061 | 5211 |
| 25062 | 5212 |
| 25063 | 5213 |
| 25064 | 5214 |
| 25065 | 5215 |
| 25066 | 5216 |
| 25068 | 5218 |
| 25069 | 5219 |
| 25070 | 5220 |
| 25071 | 5221 |
| 25073 | 5223 |
| 25074 | 5224 |
| 25075 | 5225 |
| 25076 | 5226 |
| 25077 | 5227 |
| 25078 | 5228 |
| 25079 | 5229 |
| 25080 | 5230 |
| 25081 | 5231 |
| 25082 | 5232 |
| 25084 | 5234 |
| 25085 | 5235 |
| 25086 | 5236 |
| 25087 | 5237 |
| 25088 | 5238 |
| 25089 | 5239 |
| 25090 | 5240 |
| 25091 | 5241 |
| 25092 | 5242 |
| 25093 | 5243 |
| 25094 | 5244 |
| 25095 | 5245 |
| 25096 | 5246 |
| 25097 | 5247 |
| 25098 | 5248 |
| 25099 | 5249 |
| 25100 | 5250 |
| 25101 | 5251 |
| 25102 | 5252 |
| 25103 | 5253 |
| 25104 | 5254 |
| 25105 | 5255 |
| 25106 | 5256 |
| 25107 | 5257 |
| 25108 | 5258 |
| 25109 | 5259 |
| 25110 | 5260 |
| 25111 | 5261 |
| 25112 | 5262 |
| 25113 | 5263 |
| 25114 | 5264 |
| 25115 | 5265 |
| 25116 | 5266 |
| 25117 | 5267 |
| 25118 | 5268 |
| 25119 | 5269 |
| 25120 | 5270 |
| 25121 | 5271 |
| 25122 | 5272 |
| 25123 | 5273 |
| 25124 | 5274 |
| 25125 | 5275 |
| 25126 | 5276 |
| 25127 | 5277 |
| | 5278 |
| 25129 | 5279 |

| | | |
|---|---|---|
| 25130 | 5280 | |
| 25131 | 5281 | 97202 |
| 25132 | 5282 | |
| 25133 | 5283 | |
| 25134 | 5284 | |
| 25135 | 5285 | |
| 25136 | 5286 | |
| 25137 | 5287 | |
| 25138 | 5288 | |
| 25139 | 5289 | |
| 25140 | 5290 | |
| 25141 | 5291 | |
| 25142 | 5292 | |
| 25143 | 5293 | |
| 25144 | 5294 | |
| 25145 | 5295 | |
| 25146 | 5296 | |
| 25147 | 5297 | |
| 25148 | 5298 | |
| 25149 | 5299 | |
| 25150 | 7500 | |
| 25151 | 7501 | |
| 25152 | 7502 | |
| 25153 | 7503 | |
| 25154 | 7504 | |
| 25155 | 7505 | |
| 25156 | 7506 | |
| 25157 | 7507 | |
| 25158 | 7508 | |
| 25159 | 7509 | |
| 25160 | 7510 | |
| 25161 | 7511 | |
| 25162 | 7512 | |
| 25163 | 7513 | |
| 25164 | 7514 | |
| 25165 | 7515 | |
| 25166 | 7516 | |
| 25167 | 7517 | |
| 25168 | 7518 | |
| 25169 | 7519 | |
| 25170 | 7520 | |
| 25171 | 7521 | |
| 25172 | 7522 | |
| 25174 | 7524 | |
| 25175 | 7525 | |
| 25176 | 7526 | |
| 25177 | 7527 | |
| 25178 | 7528 | |
| 25179 | 7529 | |
| 25180 | 7530 | |
| 25181 | 7531 | |
| 25182 | 7532 | |
| 25183 | 7533 | |
| 25184 | 7534 | |
| 25186 | 7536 | |
| 25187 | 7537 | |
| 25188 | 7538 | |
| 25189 | 7539 | |
| 25190 | 7540 | |
| 25192 | 7542 | |
| 25193 | 7543 | |
| 25194 | 7544 | |
| 25195 | 7545 | |
| 25196 | 7546 | |
| 25197 | 7547 | |
| 25198 | 7548 | |
| 25199 | 7549 | |
| 25200 | 7550 | |
| 25201 | 7551 | |
| 25202 | 7552 | |
| 25203 | 7553 | |
| 25204 | 7554 | |
| 25205 | 7555 | |
| 25206 | 7556 | |
| 25207 | 7557 | |
| 25208 | 7558 | |
| 25209 | 7559 | |
| 25210 | 7560 | |
| 25211 | 7561 | |
| 25212 | 7562 | |
| 25213 | 7563 | |
| 25214 | 7564 | |
| 25215 | 7565 | |
| 25216 | 7566 | |
| 25217 | 7567 | |
| 25218 | 7568 | |
| 25219 | 7569 | |
| 25220 | 7570 | |
| 25221 | 7571 | |
| 25222 | 7572 | |
| 25223 | 7573 | |
| 25224 | 7574 | |
| 25225 | 7575 | |
| 25226 | 7576 | |
| 25227 | 7577 | |
| 25228 | 7578 | |
| 25229 | 7579 | |
| 25230 | 7580 | |
| 25231 | 7581 | |
| 25232 | 7582 | |
| 25233 | 7583 | |
| 25234 | 7584 | |
| 25235 | 7585 | |
| 25236 | 7586 | |
| 25237 | 7587 | |
| 25238 | 7588 | |
| 25239 | 7589 | |
| 25240 | 7590 | |
| 25241 | 7591 | |
| 25242 | 7592 | |
| 25243 | 7593 | |
| 25245 | 7595 | |
| 25246 | 7596 | |
| 25247 | 7597 | |
| 25248 | 7598 | |
| 25249 | 7599 | |
| 25250 | 7600 | |
| 25251 | 7601 | |
| 25252 | 7602 | |
| 25253 | 7603 | |
| 25254 | 7604 | |
| | 7605 | |
| 25256 | 7606 | |
| 25257 | 7607 | |
| 25258 | 7608 | |
| 25259 | 7609 | |
| 25260 | 7610 | |
| 25261 | 7611 | |
| 25263 | 7613 | |
| 25264 | 7614 | |
| 25266 | 7616 | |
| 25267 | 7617 | |
| 25269 | 7619 | |
| 25270 | 7620 | |
| 25271 | 7621 | |
| 25272 | 7622 | |
| 25273 | 7623 | |
| 25274 | 7624 | |
| 25275 | 7625 | |
| 25277 | 7627 | |
| 25280 | 7630 | |
| 25281 | 7631 | |
| 25282 | 7632 | |
| 25284 | 7634 | |
| 25285 | 7635 | |
| 25287 | 7637 | |
| 25288 | 7638 | |
| 25289 | 7639 | |
| 25290 | 7640 | |
| 25291 | 7641 | |
| 25292 | 7642 | |
| 25293 | 7643 | |

**Class 25 Type 2 diesel-electric Bo-Bo (Continued...)**

| | | |
|---|---|---|
| 25294 | 7644 | |
| 25295 | 7645 | |
| 25298 | 7648 | |
| 25299 | 7649 | |
| 25300 | 7650 | |
| 25301 | 7651 | |
| 25302 | 7652 | |
| 25303 | 7653 | |
| 25304 | 7654 | |
| 25305 | 7655 | 97251 |
| 25306 | 7656 | |
| 25308 | 7658 | |
| 25310 | 7660 | 97250 |
| 25311 | 7661 | |
| 25312 | 7662 | |
| 25314 | 7664 | 97252 |
| 25317 | 7667 | |
| 25318 | 7668 | |
| 25319 | 7669 | |
| 25320 | 7670 | |
| 25321 | 7671 | |
| 25323 | 7673 | |
| 25324 | 7674 | |
| 25325 | 7675 | |
| 25326 | 7676 | |
| 25327 | 7677 | |
| 25902 | 25268 | 7618 |
| 25903 | 25276 | 7626 |
| 25905 | 25286 | 7636 |
| 25906 | 25296 | 7646 |
| 25907 | 25297 | 7647 |
| 25908 | 25307 | 7657 |
| 25910 | 25315 | 7665 |
| 25911 | 25316 | 7666 |

**Class 26 Type 2 diesel-electric Bo-Bo**

| | |
|---|---|
| 26003 | 5303 |
| 26005 | 5305 |
| 26006 | 5306 |
| 26008 | 5308 |
| 26009 | 5309 |
| 26012 | 5312 |
| 26013 | 5313 |
| 26015 | 5315 |
| 26016 | 5316 |
| 26017 | 5317 |
| 26018 | 5318 |
| 26019 | 5319 |
| 26020 | 5307 |
| 26021 | 5321 |
| 26022 | 5322 |
| 26023 | 5323 |
| 26026 | 5326 |
| 26027 | 5327 |
| | 5328 |
| 26028 | 5320 |
| 26029 | 5329 |
| 26030 | 5330 |
| 26031 | 5331 |
| 26032 | 5332 |
| 26033 | 5333 |
| 26034 | 5334 |
| 26036 | 5336 |
| 26037 | 5337 |
| 26039 | 5339 |
| 26041 | 5341 |
| 26042 | 5342 |
| 26044 | 5344 |
| 26045 | 5345 |
| 26046 | 5346 |

**Class 27 Type 2 diesel-electric Bo-Bo**

| | | | |
|---|---|---|---|
| 27002 | 5348 | | |
| 27003 | 5349 | | |
| 27004 | 5350 | | |
| 27006 | 5352 | | |
| 27008 | 5354 | | |
| 27009 | 5355 | | |
| 27010 | 5356 | | |
| 27011 | 5357 | | |
| 27012 | 5358 | | |
| 27013 | 5359 | | |
| 27014 | 5360 | | |
| 27015 | 5361 | | |
| 27016 | 5362 | | |
| 27017 | 5363 | | |
| 27018 | 5364 | | |
| 27019 | 5365 | | |
| 27020 | 5366 | | |
| 27021 | 5367 | | |
| 27022 | 5368 | | |
| 27023 | 5369 | | |
| 27025 | 5371 | | |
| 27026 | 5372 | | |
| 27027 | 5373 | | |
| 27028 | 5375 | | |
| 27029 | 5376 | | |
| 27030 | 5377 | | |
| 27031 | 5378 | | |
| 27032 | 5379 | | |
| 27033 | 5381 | | |
| 27034 | 5382 | | |
| | 5383 | | |
| 27035 | 5384 | | |
| 27036 | 5385 | | |
| 27037 | 5389 | | |
| 27038 | 5390 | | |
| 27039 | 5398 | | |
| 27040 | 5402 | | |
| 27041 | 5405 | | |
| 27042 | 5406 | | |
| 27043 | 5414 | | |
| 27044 | 5415 | | |
| 27045 | 27101 | 5374 | |
| 27046 | 27102 | 5380 | |
| 27047 | 27103 | 27118 | 5413 |
| 27048 | 27104 | 5387 | |
| 27049 | 27105 | 5388 | |
| 27051 | 27107 | 5395 | |
| 27052 | 27108 | 5396 | |
| 27053 | 27109 | 5397 | |
| 27054 | 27110 | 5399 | |
| 27055 | 27111 | 5400 | |
| 27058 | 27204 | 27122 | 5403 |
| 27063 | 27209 | 27115 | 5408 |
| 27064 | 27210 | 27116 | 5409 |
| 27065 | 27211 | 27117 | 5411 |
| 27201 | 27119 | 5391 | |
| 27202 | 27120 | 5392 | |
| 27203 | 27121 | 5393 | |
| 27206 | 27124 | 5412 | |
| 27207 | ADB968025 | 27113 | 5404 |
| 27208 | 27114 | 5407 | |

Note: Number 27103 was used twice

**Class 28 Type 2 diesel-electric Co-Bo**

5700
5701
5702
5703
5704
5706
5707
5708
5709
5710
5711
5712
5713
5714
5715

5716
5717
5718
5719

**Class 29 Type 2 diesel-electric Bo-Bo**

6100
6101
6102
6103
6106
6107
6108
6112
6113
6114
6116
6119
6121
6123
6124
6129
6130
6132
6133
6137

**Class 31 Type 2 diesel-electric A1A-A1A**

| | | |
|---|---|---|
| 31001 | 5501 | |
| 31002 | 5502 | ADB968014 |
| 31003 | 5503 | |
| 31004 | 5504 | |
| 31005 | 5505 | |
| 31006 | 5506 | |
| 31007 | 5507 | |
| 31008 | 5508 | ADB968016 |
| 31009 | 5509 | |
| 31010 | 5510 | |
| 31011 | 5511 | |
| 31012 | 5512 | |
| 31013 | 5513 | |
| 31014 | 5514 | ADB968015 |
| 31015 | 5515 | |
| 31016 | 5516 | |
| 31017 | 5517 | |
| 31019 | 5519 | |
| 31102 | 5520 | |
| 31103 | 5521 | |
| 31107 | 5525 | |
| 31109 | 5527 | |
| 31110 | 5528 | |
| 31111 | 5529 | |
| 31112 | 5530 | |
| 31113 | 5531 | |
| 31116 | 5534 | |
| 31117 | 5535 | |
| 31118 | 5536 | |
| 31120 | 5538 | |
| 31121 | 5539 | |
| 31122 | 5540 | |
| 31123 | 5541 | |
| 31124 | 5542 | |
| 31125 | 5543 | |
| 31126 | 5544 | |
| 31127 | 5545 | |
| 31131 | 5549 | |
| 31132 | 5550 | |
| 31134 | 5552 | |
| 31135 | 5553 | |
| 31136 | 5554 | |
| 31138 | 5556 | |
| 31141 | 5559 | |
| 31142 | 5560 | |
| 31143 | 5561 | |
| 31144 | 5562 | |
| 31145 | 5563 | |
| 31146 | 5564 | |
| 31147 | 5565 | |
| 31149 | 5567 | |
| 31150 | 5568 | |
| 31152 | 5570 | |
| 31154 | 5572 | |
| 31155 | 5573 | |
| 31156 | 5574 | |
| 31158 | 5576 | |
| 31159 | 5577 | |
| 31160 | 5578 | |
| 31164 | 5582 | |
| 31165 | 5583 | |
| 31166 | 5584 | |
| 31167 | 5585 | |
| 31168 | 5586 | |
| 31170 | 5588 | |
| 31171 | 5590 | |
| 31173 | 5593 | |
| 31174 | 5594 | |
| 31175 | 5595 | |
| 31176 | 5597 | |
| 31178 | 5599 | |
| 31180 | 5601 | |
| 31181 | 5602 | |
| 31183 | 5604 | |
| 31184 | 5607 | |
| 31185 | 5608 | |
| 31187 | 5610 | |
| 31188 | 5611 | |
| 31189 | 5612 | |
| 31192 | 5615 | |
| 31195 | 5619 | |
| 31196 | 5620 | |
| 31198 | 5622 | |
| 31199 | 5623 | |
| 31200 | 5624 | |
| 31201 | 5625 | |
| 31202 | 5626 | |
| 31205 | 5629 | |
| 31208 | 5632 | |
| 31209 | 5633 | |
| 31212 | 5636 | |
| 31214 | 5638 | |
| 31215 | 5639 | |
| 31217 | 5642 | |
| 31218 | 5643 | |
| 31219 | 5644 | |
| 31221 | 5647 | |
| 31222 | 5648 | |
| 31223 | 5649 | |
| 31224 | 5650 | |
| 31225 | 5651 | |
| 31226 | 5652 | |
| 31227 | 5653 | |
| 31229 | 5655 | |
| 31230 | 5657 | |
| 31231 | 5658 | |
| 31232 | 5659 | |
| 31234 | 5661 | |
| 31237 | 5664 | |
| 31238 | 5665 | |
| 31240 | 5667 | |
| 31241 | 5668 | |
| 31242 | 5670 | |
| 31243 | 5671 | |
| 31244 | 5672 | |
| 31245 | 5673 | |
| 31247 | 5675 | |
| 31248 | 5676 | |
| 31249 | 5677 | |
| 31250 | 5678 | |
| 31252 | 5680 | |
| 31254 | 5682 | |
| 31257 | 5685 | |
| 31259 | 5687 | |
| 31260 | 5688 | |

**Class 31 Type 2 diesel-electric A1A-A1A (Continued...)**

| | | | |
|---|---|---|---|
| 31261 | 5689 | | |
| 31262 | 5690 | | |
| 31263 | 5693 | | |
| 31264 | 5694 | | |
| 31268 | 5698 | | |
| 31272 | 5802 | | |
| 31273 | 5803 | | |
| 31275 | 5805 | | |
| 31276 | 5806 | | |
| 31278 | 5808 | | |
| 31280 | 5810 | | |
| 31281 | 5811 | | |
| 31282 | 5813 | | |
| 31283 | 5815 | | |
| 31284 | 5816 | | |
| 31286 | 5818 | | |
| 31287 | 5819 | | |
| 31288 | 5820 | | |
| 31290 | 5822 | | |
| 31292 | 5825 | | |
| 31293 | 5826 | | |
| 31294 | 5827 | | |
| 31296 | 5829 | | |
| 31298 | 5831 | 97203 | |
| 31299 | 5832 | | |
| 31301 | 5834 | | |
| 31302 | 5835 | | |
| 31304 | 5837 | | |
| 31305 | 5838 | | |
| 31306 | 5839 | | |
| 31308 | 5841 | | |
| 31309 | 5843 | | |
| 31311 | 5845 | | |
| 31312 | 5846 | | |
| 31313 | 5847 | | |
| 31314 | 5848 | | |
| 31317 | 5851 | | |
| 31319 | 5853 | | |
| 31320 | 5854 | | |
| 31322 | 5857 | | |
| 31323 | 5858 | | |
| 31324 | 5859 | | |
| 31400 | 31161 | 5579 | |
| 31401 | 5589 | | |
| 31402 | 5592 | | |
| 31403 | 5596 | | |
| 31404 | 5605 | | |
| 31405 | 5606 | | |
| 31406 | 5616 | | |
| 31407 | 31507 | 5640 | |
| 31408 | 5646 | | |
| 31409 | 5656 | | |
| 31410 | 5669 | | |
| 31411 | 31511 | 5691 | |
| 31412 | 31512 | 5692 | |
| 31413 | 5812 | | |
| 31415 | 5824 | | |
| 31417 | 5856 | | |
| 31420 | 31172 | 5591 | |
| 31421 | 31140 | 5558 | |
| 31422 | 31522 | 31310 | 5844 |
| 31423 | 31197 | 5621 | |
| 31425 | 31274 | 5804 | |
| 31426 | 31526 | 31193 | 5617 |
| 31427 | 31194 | 5618 | |
| 31428 | 31211 | 5635 | |
| 31429 | 31269 | 5699 | |
| 31432 | 31153 | 5571 | |
| 31433 | 31533 | 31236 | 5663 |
| 31434 | 31258 | 5686 | |
| 31436 | 31151 | 5569 | |
| 31437 | 31537 | 31182 | 5603 |
| 31439 | 31239 | 5666 | |
| 31440 | 31204 | 5628 | |
| 31442 | 31251 | 5679 | |
| 31443 | 31177 | 5598 | |
| 31444 | 31544 | 31137 | 5555 |
| 31450 | 31133 | 5551 | |
| 31455 | 31555 | 31246 | 5674 |
| 31457 | 31169 | 5587 | |
| 31460 | 31266 | 5696 | |
| 31462 | 31315 | 5849 | |
| 31464 | 31325 | 5860 | |
| 31467 | 31216 | 5641 | |
| 31516 | 31416 | 5842 | |
| 31519 | 31419 | 5697 | |
| 31524 | 31424 | 31157 | 5575 |
| 31531 | 31431 | 31253 | 5681 |
| 31541 | 31441 | 31220 | 5645 |
| 31545 | 31445 | 31300 | 5833 |
| 31546 | 31446 | 31316 | 5850 |
| 31547 | 31447 | 31295 | 5828 |
| 31548 | 31448 | 31148 | 5566 |
| 31549 | 31449 | 31307 | 5840 |
| 31551 | 31451 | 31318 | 5852 |
| 31553 | 31453 | 31114 | 5532 |
| 31556 | 31456 | 31291 | 5823 |
| 31558 | 31458 | 31303 | 5836 |
| 31569 | 31469 | 31277 | 5807 |
| 31970 | 97204 | 31326 | 5861 |

**Class 33 Type 3 diesel-electric Bo-Bo**

| | |
|---|---|
| 33001 | 6500 |
| | 6502 |
| 33003 | 6503 |
| 33004 | 6504 |
| 33005 | 6505 |
| 33006 | 6506 |
| 33007 | 6507 |
| 33009 | 6509 |
| 33010 | 6510 |
| 33011 | 6512 |
| 33013 | 6518 |
| 33014 | 6522 |
| 33015 | 6523 |
| 33016 | 6524 |
| 33017 | 6526 |
| 33020 | 6537 |
| 33022 | 6540 |
| 33023 | 6541 |
| 33024 | 6542 |
| 33026 | 6544 |
| 33027 | 6545 |
| 33028 | 6546 |
| 33031 | 6549 |
| 33032 | 6550 |
| 33033 | 6551 |
| 33034 | 6552 |
| 33036 | 6554 |
| 33037 | 6555 |
| 33038 | 6556 |
| 33039 | 6557 |
| 33040 | 6558 |
| 33041 | 6559 |
| 33042 | 6560 |
| 33043 | 6561 |
| 33044 | 6562 |
| 33045 | 6563 |
| 33047 | 6565 |
| 33049 | 6567 |
| 33050 | 6568 |
| 33051 | 6569 |
| 33054 | 6572 |
| 33055 | 6573 |
| 33056 | 3574 |
| | 6576 |
| 33058 | 6577 |
| 33059 | 6578 |
| 33060 | 6579 |
| 33061 | 6581 |
| 33062 | 6582 |

| | | |
|---|---|---|
| 33064 | 6584 | |
| 33101 | 6511 | |
| 33104 | 6516 | |
| 33105 | 6517 | |
| 33106 | 6519 | |
| 33107 | 6520 | |
| 33112 | 6529 | |
| 33113 | 6531 | |
| 33114 | 6532 | |
| 33115 | 83301 | 6533 |
| 33118 | 6538 | |
| 33119 | 6580 | |
| 33203 | 6588 | |
| 33204 | 6589 | |
| 33205 | 33302 | 6590 |
| 33206 | 6591 | |
| 33209 | 6594 | |
| 33210 | 6595 | |
| 33211 | 6596 | |
| 33212 | 6597 | |

**Class 35 Type 3 diesel-hydraulic B-B**

| | |
|---|---|
| 7000 | |
| 7001 | |
| 7002 | |
| 7003 | |
| 7004 | |
| 7005 | |
| 7006 | |
| 7007 | |
| 7008 | |
| 7009 | |
| 7010 | |
| 7011 | |
| 7012 | |
| 7013 | |
| 7014 | |
| 7015 | |
| 7016 | |
| 7019 | |
| 7020 | |
| 7021 | |
| 7022 | |
| 7023 | |
| 7024 | |
| 7025 | |
| 7026 | |
| 7027 | |
| 7028 | |
| 7030 | |
| 7031 | |
| 7032 | |
| 7033 | |
| 7034 | |
| 7035 | |
| 7036 | |
| 7037 | |
| 7038 | |
| 7039 | |
| 7040 | |
| 7041 | |
| 7042 | |
| 7043 | |
| 7044 | |
| 7045 | |
| 7046 | |
| 7047 | |
| 7048 | |
| 7049 | |
| 7050 | |
| 7051 | |
| 7052 | |
| 7053 | |
| 7054 | |
| 7055 | DB968004 |
| 7056 | |
| 7057 | |
| 7058 | |
| 7059 | |
| 7060 | |
| 7061 | |
| 7062 | |
| 7063 | |
| 7064 | |
| 7065 | |
| 7066 | |
| 7067 | |
| 7068 | |
| 7069 | |
| 7070 | |
| 7071 | |
| 7072 | |
| 7073 | |
| 7074 | |
| 7075 | |
| 7077 | |
| 7078 | |
| 7079 | |
| 7080 | |
| 7081 | |
| 7082 | |
| 7083 | |
| 7084 | |
| 7085 | |
| 7086 | |
| 7087 | |
| 7088 | |
| 7089 | TDB968005 |
| 7090 | |
| 7091 | |
| 7092 | |
| 7093 | |
| 7094 | |
| 7095 | |
| 7096 | |
| 7097 | |
| 7098 | |
| 7099 | |
| 7100 | |

**Class 37 Type 3 diesel-electric Co-Co**

| | | |
|---|---|---|
| 37004 | 6704 | |
| 37008 | 37352 | 6708 |
| 37010 | 6710 | |
| 37011 | 6711 | |
| 37012 | 6712 | |
| 37013 | 6713 | |
| 37019 | 6719 | |
| 37026 | 37320 | 6726 |
| 37031 | 6731 | |
| 37035 | 6735 | |
| 37040 | 6740 | |
| 37043 | 37354 | 6743 |
| 37045 | 37355 | 6745 |
| 37046 | 6746 | |
| 37047 | 6747 | |
| 37048 | 6748 | |
| 37051 | 6751 | |
| 37054 | 6754 | |
| 37055 | 6755 | |
| 37058 | 6758 | |
| 37062 | 6762 | |
| 37063 | 6763 | |
| 37065 | 6765 | |
| 37066 | 6766 | |
| 37068 | 37356 | 6768 |
| 37070 | 6770 | |
| 37071 | 6771 | |
| 37072 | 6772 | |
| 37073 | 6773 | |
| 37074 | 6774 | |
| 37077 | 6777 | |

**Class 37 Type 3 diesel-electric Co-Co (Continued…)**

| | | | |
|---|---|---|---|
| 37078 | 6778 | | |
| 37079 | 37357 | 6779 | |
| 37080 | 6780 | | |
| 37083 | 6783 | | |
| 37087 | 6787 | | |
| 37088 | 37323 | 6788 | |
| 37092 | 6792 | | |
| 37095 | 6795 | | |
| 37096 | 6796 | | |
| 37098 | 6798 | | |
| 37104 | 6804 | | |
| 37106 | 6806 | | |
| 37107 | 6807 | | |
| 37110 | 6810 | | |
| 37111 | 37326 | 6811 | |
| 37113 | 6813 | | |
| 37114 | 6814 | | |
| 37131 | 6831 | | |
| 37133 | 6833 | | |
| 37137 | 37312 | 6837 | |
| 37138 | 6838 | | |
| 37139 | 6839 | | |
| 37140 | 6840 | | |
| 37141 | 6841 | | |
| 37144 | 6844 | | |
| 37153 | 6853 | | |
| 37154 | 6854 | | |
| 37156 | 37311 | 6856 | |
| 37158 | 6858 | | |
| 37162 | 6862 | | |
| 37174 | 6874 | | |
| 37184 | 6884 | | |
| 37185 | 6885 | | |
| 37191 | 6891 | | |
| 37194 | 6894 | | |
| 37196 | 6896 | | |
| 37197 | 6897 | | |
| 37201 | 6901 | | |
| 37203 | 6903 | | |
| 37209 | 6909 | | |
| 37211 | 6911 | | |
| 37212 | 6912 | | |
| 37213 | 6913 | | |
| 37220 | 6920 | | |
| 37221 | 6921 | | |
| 37222 | 6922 | | |
| 37223 | 6923 | | |
| 37225 | 6925 | | |
| 37229 | 6929 | | |
| 37230 | 6930 | | |
| 37232 | 6932 | | |
| 37235 | 6935 | | |
| 37238 | 6938 | | |
| 37241 | 6941 | | |
| 37242 | 6942 | | |
| 37244 | 6944 | | |
| 37245 | 6945 | | |
| 37251 | 6951 | | |
| 37252 | 6952 | | |
| 37260 | 6960 | | |
| 37262 | 6962 | | |
| 37273 | 37306 | 6606 | |
| 37278 | 6978 | | |
| 37280 | 6980 | | |
| | 6983 | | |
| 37293 | 6993 | | |
| 37298 | 6998 | | |
| 37330 | 37128 | 6828 | |
| 37331 | 37202 | 6902 | |
| 37332 | 37239 | 6939 | |
| 37333 | 37271 | 37303 | 6603 |
| 37334 | 37272 | 37304 | 6604 |
| 37335 | 37285 | 6985 | |
| 37341 | 37015 | 6715 | |
| 37343 | 37049 | 37322 | 6749 |

| | | | |
|---|---|---|---|
| 37344 | 37053 | 6753 | |
| 37345 | 37101 | 6801 | |
| 37351 | 37002 | 6702 | |
| 37358 | 37091 | 6791 | |
| 37359 | 37118 | 6818 | |
| 37370 | 37127 | 6827 | |
| 37371 | 37147 | 6847 | |
| 37372 | 37159 | 6859* | |
| 37373 | 37160 | 6860 | |
| 37375 | 37193 | 6893 | |
| 37376 | 37199 | 6899 | |
| 37377 | 37200 | 6900 | |
| 37378 | 37204 | 6904 | |
| 37379 | 37226 | 6926 | |
| 37381 | 37284 | 6984 | |
| 37382 | 37145 | 37313 | 6845 |
| 37383 | 37167 | 6867 | |
| 37384 | 37258 | 6958 | |
| 37404 | 37286 | 6986 | |
| 37406 | 37295 | 6995 | |
| 37408 | 37289 | 6989 | |
| 37410 | 37273 | 6973 | |
| 37411 | 37290 | 6990 | |
| 37412 | 37301 | 6601 | |
| 37413 | 37276 | 6976 | |
| 37414 | 37287 | 6987 | |
| 37415 | 37277 | 6977 | |
| 37416 | 37302 | 6602 | |
| 37417 | 37269 | 6969 | |
| 37420 | 37297 | 6997 | |
| 37426 | 37299 | 6999 | |
| 37427 | 37288 | 6988 | |
| 37428 | 37281 | 6981 | |
| 37429 | 37300 | 6600 | |
| 37430 | 37265 | 6965 | |
| 37431 | 37272 | 6972 | |
| 37505 | 37028 | 6728 | |
| 37509 | 37093 | 6793 | |
| 37513 | 37056 | 6756 | |
| 37515 | 37064 | 6764 | |
| 37519 | 37027 | 6727 | |
| 37520 | 37041 | 6741 | |
| 37671 | 37247 | 6947 | |
| 37672 | 37189 | 6889 | |
| 37673 | 37132 | 6832 | |
| 37675 | 37164 | 6864 | |
| 37677 | 37121 | 6821 | |
| 37678 | 37256 | 6956 | |
| 37680 | 37224 | 6924 | |
| 37681 | 37130 | 6830 | |
| 37682 | 37236 | 6936 | |
| 37683 | 37187 | 6877 | |
| 37684 | 37134 | 6834 | |
| 37686 | 37172 | 6872 | |
| 37689 | 37195 | 6895 | |
| 37692 | 37122 | 6822 | |
| 37693 | 37210 | 6910 | |
| 37694 | 37192 | 6892 | |
| 37695 | 37157 | 6857 | |
| 37696 | 37228 | 6928 | |
| 37697 | 37243 | 6943 | |
| 37698 | 37246 | 6946 | |
| 37699 | 37253 | 6953 | |
| 37701 | 37030 | 6730 | |
| 37702 | 37020 | 6720 | |
| 37704 | 37034 | 6734 | |
| 37705 | 37060 | 6760 | |
| 37707 | 37001 | 6701 | |
| 37708 | 37089 | 6789 | |
| 37709 | 37014 | 6714 | |
| 37711 | 37085 | 6785 | |
| 37713 | 37052 | 6752 | |
| 37715 | 37021 | 6721 | |
| 37717 | 37050 | 6750 | |
| 37718 | 37084 | 6784 | |
| 37719 | 37033 | 6733 | |

| | | |
|---|---|---|
| 37796 | 37105 | 6805 |
| 37797 | 37081 | 6781 |
| 37798 | 37006 | 6706 |
| 37799 | 37061 | 6761 |
| 37801 | 37173 | 6873 |
| 37802 | 37163 | 6863 |
| 37803 | 37208 | 6908 |
| 37883 | 37176 | 6876 |
| 37885 | 37177 | 6877 |
| 37886 | 37180 | 6880 |
| 37887 | 37120 | 6820 |
| 37888 | 37135 | 6835 |
| 37889 | 37233 | 6933 |
| 37890 | 37168 | 6868 |
| 37891 | 37166 | 6866 |
| 37892 | 37149 | 6849 |
| 37893 | 37237 | 6937 |
| 37894 | 37124 | 6824 |
| 37895 | 37283 | 6819 |
| 37896 | 37231 | 6931 |
| 37897 | 37155 | 6855 |
| 37898 | 37186 | 6886 |
| 37899 | 37161 | 6861 |
| 37902 | 37148 | 6848 |
| 37903 | 37249 | 6949 |
| 37904 | 37125 | 6825 |

Note: Numbers 37271-274 were used twice
*37372 donated parts of its body to the construction of D5910

**Class 40 Type 4 diesel-electric 1Co-Co1**

| | | |
|---|---|---|
| 40001 | 201 | |
| 40002 | 202 | |
| 40003 | 203 | |
| 40004 | 204 | |
| 40005 | 205 | |
| 40006 | 206 | |
| 40007 | 207 | |
| 40008 | 208 | |
| 40009 | 209 | |
| 40010 | 210 | |
| 40011 | 211 | |
| 40014 | 214 | |
| 40015 | 215 | |
| 40016 | 216 | |
| 40017 | 217 | |
| 40018 | 218 | |
| 40019 | 219 | |
| 40020 | 220 | |
| 40021 | 221 | |
| 40022 | 222 | |
| 40023 | 223 | |
| 40024 | 224 | |
| 40025 | 225 | |
| 40026 | 226 | |
| 40027 | 227 | |
| 40028 | 228 | |
| 40029 | 229 | |
| 40030 | 230 | |
| 40031 | 231 | |
| 40032 | 232 | |
| 40033 | 233 | |
| 40034 | 234 | |
| 40035 | 235 | |
| 40036 | 236 | |
| 40037 | 237 | |
| 40038 | 238 | |
| 40039 | 239 | |
| 40040 | 240 | |
| 40041 | 241 | |
| 40042 | 242 | |
| 40043 | 243 | |
| 40044 | 244 | |
| 40045 | 245 | |
| 40046 | 246 | |
| 40047 | 247 | |
| 40048 | 248 | |
| 40049 | 249 | |
| 40050 | 250 | |
| 40051 | 251 | |
| 40052 | 252 | |
| 40053 | 253 | |
| 40054 | 254 | |
| 40055 | 255 | |
| 40056 | 256 | |
| 40057 | 257 | |
| 40058 | 258 | |
| 40059 | 259 | |
| 40060 | 260 | 97405 |
| 40061 | 261 | |
| 40062 | 262 | |
| 40063 | 263 | |
| 40064 | 264 | |
| 40065 | 265 | |
| 40066 | 266 | |
| 40067 | 267 | |
| 40068 | 268 | |
| 40069 | 269 | |
| 40070 | 270 | |
| 40071 | 271 | |
| 40072 | 272 | |
| 40073 | 273 | |
| 40074 | 274 | |
| 40075 | 275 | |
| 40076 | 276 | |
| 40077 | 277 | |
| 40078 | 278 | |
| 40079 | 279 | |
| 40080 | 280 | |
| 40081 | 281 | |
| 40082 | 282 | |
| 40083 | 283 | |
| 40084 | 284 | |
| 40085 | 285 | |
| 40086 | 286 | |
| 40087 | 287 | |
| 40088 | 288 | |
| 40089 | 289 | |
| 40090 | 290 | |
| 40091 | 291 | |
| 40092 | 292 | |
| 40093 | 293 | |
| 40094 | 294 | |
| 40095 | 295 | |
| 40096 | 296 | |
| 40097 | 297 | |
| 40098 | 298 | |
| 40099 | 299 | |
| 40100 | 300 | |
| 40101 | 301 | |
| 40102 | 302 | |
| 40103 | 303 | |
| 40104 | 304 | |
| 40105 | 305 | |
| 40107 | 307 | |
| 40108 | 308 | |
| 40109 | 309 | |
| 40110 | 310 | |
| 40111 | 311 | |
| 40112 | 312 | |
| 40113 | 313 | |
| 40114 | 314 | |
| 40115 | 315 | |
| 40116 | 316 | |
| 40117 | 317 | |
| 40119 | 319 | |
| 40120 | 320 | |
| 40121 | 321 | |
| | 322 | |
| 40123 | 323 | |
| 40124 | 324 | |
| 40125 | 325 | |

**Class 40 Type 4 diesel-electric 1Co-Co1 (Continued...)**

| | |
|---|---|
| 40126 | 326 |
| 40127 | 327 |
| 40128 | 328 |
| 40129 | 329 |
| 40130 | 330 |
| 40131 | 331 |
| 40132 | 332 |
| 40133 | 333 |
| 40134 | 334 |
| 40136 | 336 |
| 40137 | 337 |
| 40138 | 338 |
| 40139 | 339 |
| 40140 | 340 |
| 40141 | 341 |
| 40142 | 342 |
| 40143 | 343 |
| 40144 | 344 |
| 40146 | 346 |
| 40147 | 347 |
| 40148 | 348 |
| 40149 | 349 |
| 40150 | 350 |
| 40151 | 351 |
| 40152 | 352 |
| 40153 | 353 |
| 40154 | 354 |
| 40155 | 355 |
| 40156 | 356 |
| 40157 | 357 |
| 40158 | 358 |
| 40159 | 359 |
| 40160 | 360 |
| 40161 | 361 |
| 40162 | 362 |
| 40163 | 363 |
| 40164 | 364 |
| 40165 | 365 |
| 40166 | 366 |
| 40167 | 367 |
| 40168 | 368 |
| 40169 | 369 |
| 40170 | 370 |
| 40171 | 371 |
| 40172 | 372 |
| 40173 | 373 |
| 40174 | 374 |
| 40175 | 375 |
| 40176 | 376 |
| 40177 | 377 |
| 40178 | 378 |
| 40179 | 379 |
| 40180 | 380 |
| 40181 | 381 |
| 40182 | 382 |
| 40183 | 383 |
| 40184 | 384 |
| 40185 | 385 |
| 40186 | 386 |
| 40187 | 387 |
| 40188 | 388 |
| 40189 | 389 |
| 40190 | 390 |
| 40191 | 391 |
| 40192 | 392 |
| 40193 | 393 |
| 40194 | 394 |
| 40195 | 395 |
| 40196 | 396 |
| 40197 | 397 |
| 40198 | 398 |
| 40199 | 399 |

**Class 41 Type 4 diesel-hydraulic A1A-A1A**

600
601
602
603
604

**Class 42 Type 4 diesel-hydraulic B-B**

800
801
802
803
804
805
806
807
808
809
810
811
812
813
814
815
816
817
818
819
820
822
823
824
825
826
827
828
829
830
831
866
867
868
869
870

**Class 43 Type 4 diesel-hydraulic B-B**

833
834
835
836
837
838
839
840
841
842
843
844
845
846
847
848
849
850
851
852
853
854
855
856
857
858
859
860
861
862
863
864
865

**Class 41/43 Type 4 diesel-electric Bo-Bo (HST power car)**

41002 43001 ADB975813

**Class 43 Type 4 diesel-electric Bo-Bo (HST power car)**

43011
43019
43173

**Class 44 Type 4 diesel-electric 1Co-Co1**

44001 1
44002 2
44003 3
44005 5
44006 6
44007 7
44009 9
44010 10

**Class 45 Type 4 diesel-electric 1Co-Co1**

45001 13
45002 29
45003 133
45004 77
45005 79
45006 89
45007 119
45008 90
45009 37
45010 112
45011 12
45012 108
45013 20
45014 137
45016 16
45017 23 ADB968024
45018 15
45019 33
45020 26
45021 25
45022 60 97409
45023 54
45024 17
45025 19
45026 21
45027 24
45028 27
45029 30 97410
45030 31
45031 36
45032 38
45033 39
45034 42 97411
45035 44
45036 45
45037 46
45038 48
45039 49
45040 50 97412
45042 57
45043 58
45044 63
45045 64
45046 68
45047 69
45048 70
45049 71
45050 72
45051 74
45052 75
45053 76
45054 95
45055 84
45056 91
45057 93
45058 97
45059 98
45061 101
45062 103
45063 104
45064 105
45065 110
45066 114 97413
45067 115
45068 118
45069 121
45070 122
45071 125
45072 127
45073 129
45074 131
45075 132
45076 134
45077 136
45101 96
45102 51
45103 116
45104 59
45106 106
45107 43
45109 85
45110 73
45111 65
45113 80
45114 94
45115 81
45116 47
45117 35
45119 34
45120 107
45121 18
45122 11
45123 52
45124 28
45126 32
45127 87
45128 113
45129 111
45130 117
45131 124
45134 126
45136 88
45137 56
45138 92
45139 109
45140 102
45141 82
45142 83
45143 62
45144 55
45145 128
45146 66
45147 41
45148 130
45150 45054 78

Note: Number 45054 was used twice

**Class 46 Type 4 diesel-electric 1Co-Co1**

46001 138
46002 139
46003 140
46004 141
46005 142
46006 143
46007 144
46008 145
46009 146
46011 148
46012 149
46013 150
46014 151
46015 152
46016 153
46017 154
46018 155

**Class 46 Type 4 diesel-electric 1Co-Co1 (Continued...)**

| | |
|---|---|
| 46019 | 156 |
| 46020 | 157 |
| 46021 | 158 |
| 46022 | 159 |
| 46023 | 160 |
| 46024 | 161 |
| 46025 | 162 |
| 46026 | 163 |
| 46027 | 164 |
| 46028 | 165 |
| 46029 | 166 |
| 46030 | 167 |
| 46031 | 168 |
| 46032 | 169 |
| 46033 | 170 |
| 46034 | 171 |
| 46036 | 173 |
| 46037 | 174 |
| 46038 | 175 |
| 46039 | 176 |
| 46040 | 177 |
| 46041 | 178 |
| 46042 | 179 |
| 46043 | 180 |
| 46044 | 181 |
| 46046 | 183 |
| 46047 | 184 |
| 46048 | 185 |
| 46049 | 186 |
| 46050 | 187 |
| 46051 | 188 |
| 46052 | 189 |
| 46053 | 190 |
| 46054 | 191 |
| 46055 | 192 |
| 46056 | 193 |

**Class 47 Type 4 diesel-electric Co-Co**

| | | |
|---|---|---|
| 47001 | 1521 | |
| 47002 | 1522 | |
| 47003 | 1523 | |
| 47005 | 1526 | |
| 47006 | 1528 | |
| 47007 | 1529 | |
| 47008 | 1530 | |
| 47009 | 1532 | |
| 47010 | 1537 | |
| 47011 | 1538 | |
| 47012 | 1539 | |
| 47013 | 1540 | |
| 47014 | 1543 | |
| 47015 | 1544 | |
| 47016 | 1546 | |
| 47017 | 1570 | |
| 47018 | 1572 | |
| 47019 | 1573 | |
| 47033 | 1613 | |
| 47049 | 1631 | |
| 47050 | 1632 | |
| 47051 | 1633 | |
| 47052 | 1634 | |
| 47053 | 1635 | |
| 47054 | 1638 | |
| 47063 | 1647 | |
| 47085 | 1670 | |
| | 1671 | |
| 47089 | 1675 | |
| 47093 | 1679 | |
| 47094 | 1680 | |
| 47095 | 1681 | |
| 47096 | 1682 | |
| 47097 | 1684 | |
| 47098 | 1685 | |
| 47099 | 1686 | |
| 47100 | 1687 | |
| 47101 | 1688 | |
| 47102 | 1690 | |
| 47103 | 1691 | |
| 47104 | 1692 | |
| 47106 | 1694 | |
| 47107 | 1695 | |
| 47108 | 1696 | |
| 47109 | 1697 | |
| 47110 | 1698 | |
| 47111 | 1699 | |
| 47112 | 1700 | |
| 47113 | 1701 | |
| 47114 | 1702 | |
| 47115 | 1703 | |
| 47116 | 1704 | |
| 47118 | 1706 | |
| 47119 | 1708 | |
| 47120 | 1709 | |
| 47121 | 1710 | |
| 47122 | 1711 | |
| 47123 | 1712 | |
| 47124 | 1714 | |
| 47125 | 1715 | |
| 47130 | 1721 | |
| 47131 | 1722 | |
| 47137 | 1729 | |
| 47140 | 1732 | |
| | 1734 | |
| 47142 | 1735 | |
| 47143 | 1736 | |
| 47144 | 1737 | |
| 47145 | 1738 | |
| 47146 | 1739 | |
| 47147 | 1740 | |
| 47148 | 1741 | |
| 47150 | 47399 | 1743 |
| 47152 | 47398 | 1745 |
| 47156 | 1749 | |
| 47157 | 1750 | |
| 47159 | 1752 | |
| 47162 | 1756 | |
| 47186 | 1781 | |
| 47188 | 1838 | |
| 47189 | 1839 | |
| 47190 | 1840 | |
| 47191 | 1841 | |
| 47193 | 1843 | |
| 47195 | 1845 | |
| 47196 | 1846 | |
| 47197 | 1847 | |
| 47198 | 1848 | |
| 47199 | 1849 | |
| 47200 | 1850 | |
| 47201 | 1851 | |
| 47202 | 1852 | |
| 47203 | 1853 | |
| 47207 | 1857 | |
| 47208 | 1858 | |
| 47210 | 1860 | |
| 47211 | 47394 | 1861 |
| 47212 | 1862 | |
| 47213 | 1863 | |
| 47214 | 1864 | |
| 47215 | 1865 | |
| 47217 | 1867 | |
| 47218 | 1868 | |
| 47219 | 1869 | |
| 47220 | 1870 | |
| 47221 | 1871 | |
| 47222 | 1872 | |
| 47223 | 1873 | |
| 47224 | 1874 | |
| 47226 | 47384 | 1902 |
| 47227 | 1903 | |
| 47228 | 1904 | |
| 47229 | 1905 | |

| | | |
|---|---|---|
| 47230 | 1906 | |
| | 1908 | |
| 47233 | 1910 | |
| 47235 | 1912 | |
| 47238 | 1915 | |
| 47241 | 1918 | |
| 47249 | 1926 | |
| 47256 | 1934 | |
| 47258 | 1938 | |
| 47275 | 1977 | |
| 47276 | 1978 | |
| 47277 | 1979 | |
| 47278 | 1980 | |
| 47279 | 1981 | |
| 47280 | 1982 | |
| 47281 | 1983 | |
| 47282 | 1984 | |
| 47283 | 1985 | |
| 47284 | 1986 | |
| 47285 | 1987 | |
| 47286 | 1988 | |
| 47287 | 1989 | |
| 47288 | 1990 | |
| 47289 | 1991 | |
| 47291 | 1993 | |
| 47293 | 1995 | |
| 47294 | 1996 | |
| 47295 | 1997 | |
| 47296 | 1998 | |
| 47297 | 1999 | |
| 47298 | 1100 | |
| 47299 | 47216 | 1866 |
| 47300 | 47468 | 1594 |
| 47301 | 1782 | |
| 47302 | 1783 | |
| 47303 | 47397 | 1784 |
| 47304 | 47392 | 1785 |
| 47305 | 1786 | |
| 47307 | 1788 | |
| 47308 | 1789 | |
| 47309 | 47389 | 1790 |
| 47310 | 1791 | |
| 47311 | 1792 | |
| 47312 | 1793 | |
| 47313 | 1794 | |
| 47314 | 47387 | 1795 |
| 47315 | 1796 | |
| 47316 | 1797 | |
| 47318 | 1799 | |
| 47319 | 1800 | |
| 47320 | 1801 | |
| 47321 | 1802 | |
| 47323 | 1804 | |
| 47324 | 1805 | |
| 47325 | 1806 | |
| 47326 | 1807 | |
| 47327 | 1808 | |
| 47328 | 47396 | 1809 |
| 47331 | 1812 | |
| 47333 | 1814 | |
| 47334 | 1815 | |
| 47335 | 1816 | |
| 47336 | 1817 | |
| 47338 | 1819 | |
| 47339 | 1820 | |
| 47340 | 1821 | |
| 47341 | 1822 | |
| 47342 | 1823 | |
| 47343 | 1824 | |
| 47344 | 1825 | |
| 47345 | 1826 | |
| 47346 | 1827 | |
| 47348 | 1829 | |
| 47351 | 1832 | |
| 47352 | 1833 | |
| 47353 | 1834 | |

| | | |
|---|---|---|
| 47354 | 1835 | |
| 47357 | 1876 | |
| 47358 | 1877 | |
| 47359 | 1878 | |
| 47360 | 1879 | |
| 47361 | 1880 | |
| 47362 | 1881 | |
| 47363 | 47385 | 1882 |
| 47365 | 1884 | |
| 47366 | 1885 | |
| 47369 | 1888 | |
| 47370 | 1889 | |
| 47373 | 1892 | |
| 47374 | 1893 | |
| 47377 | 1896 | |
| 47378 | 47386 | 1897 |
| 47379 | 1898 | |
| 47380 | 1899 | |
| 47381 | 1900 | |
| 47403 | 1502 | |
| 47404 | 1503 | |
| 47405 | 1504 | |
| 47406 | 1505 | |
| 47407 | 1506 | |
| 47408 | 1507 | |
| 47409 | 1508 | |
| 47410 | 1509 | |
| 47411 | 1510 | |
| 47412 | 1511 | |
| 47413 | 1512 | |
| 47414 | 1513 | |
| 47415 | 1514 | |
| 47416 | 1515 | |
| 47418 | 1517 | |
| 47419 | 1518 | |
| 47420 | 1519 | |
| 47421 | 1520 | |
| 47422 | 1525 | |
| 47423 | 1527 | |
| 47424 | 1531 | |
| 47425 | 1533 | |
| 47426 | 1534 | |
| 47427 | 1535 | |
| 47428 | 1536 | |
| 47429 | 1541 | |
| 47430 | 1542 | |
| 47431 | 1545 | |
| 47432 | 1547 | |
| 47433 | 1548 | |
| 47434 | 1549 | |
| 47435 | 1550 | |
| 47436 | 1552 | |
| 47437 | 1553 | |
| 47438 | 1554 | |
| 47439 | 1555 | |
| 47440 | 1556 | |
| 47441 | 1557 | |
| 47442 | 1558 | |
| 47443 | 1559 | |
| 47444 | 1560 | |
| 47445 | 1561 | |
| | 1562 | |
| 47446 | 1563 | |
| 47447 | 1564 | |
| 47448 | 1565 | |
| 47450 | 1567 | |
| 47451 | 1568 | |
| 47452 | 1569 | |
| 47453 | 1571 | |
| 47454 | 1574 | |
| 47455 | 1575 | |
| 47456 | 1576 | |
| 47457 | 1577 | |
| 47458 | 1578 | |
| 47459 | 1579 | |
| 47460 | 1580 | |

**Class 47 Type 4 diesel-electric Co-Co (Continued...)**

| | | | | |
|---|---|---|---|---|
| 47461 | 1581 | | | |
| 47462 | 1582 | | | |
| 47463 | 1586 | | | |
| 47464 | 1587 | | | |
| 47465 | 1589 | | | |
| 47466 | 1590 | | | |
| 47467 | 1593 | | | |
| 47469 | 1595 | | | |
| 47470 | 1596 | | | |
| 47471 | 1598 | | | |
| 47472 | 97472 | 1600 | | |
| 47473 | 1601 | | | |
| 47474 | 1602 | | | |
| 47475 | 1603 | | | |
| 47476 | 1604 | | | |
| 47477 | 1607 | | | |
| 47478 | 1608 | | | |
| 47479 | 1612 | | | |
| 47481 | 1627 | | | |
| 47482 | 1636 | | | |
| 47483 | 1637 | | | |
| 47485 | 1683 | | | |
| 47486 | 1689 | | | |
| 47487 | 1707 | | | |
| 47489 | 1716 | | | |
| 47508 | 1952 | | | |
| 47509 | 1953 | | | |
| 47512 | 1958 | | | |
| 47513 | 1959 | | | |
| 47515 | 1961 | | | |
| 47518 | 1101 | | | |
| 47519 | 1102 | | | |
| 47520 | 1103 | | | |
| 47521 | 1104 | | | |
| 47522 | 1105 | | | |
| 47523 | 1106 | | | |
| 47525 | 1108 | | | |
| 47527 | 1110 | | | |
| 47528 | 1111 | | | |
| 47529 | 1551 | | | |
| 47530 | 1930 | | | |
| 47532 | 1641 | | | |
| 47533 | 1651 | | | |
| 47534 | 1678 | | | |
| 47535 | 1649 | | | |
| 47536 | 1655 | | | |
| 47538 | 1669 | ADB968035 | | |
| 47539 | 1718 | | | |
| 47540 | 47975 | 1723 | | |
| 47542 | 1585 | | | |
| 47543 | 1588 | | | |
| 47544 | 1592 | | | |
| 47547 | 1642 | | | |
| 47549 | 47133 | 1724 | | |
| 47550 | 1731 | | | |
| 47555 | 47126 | 1717 | | |
| 47565 | 47039 | 1620 | | |
| 47566 | 47043 | 1624 | | |
| 47572 | 47168 | 1763 | | |
| 47574 | 47174 | 1769 | | |
| 47575 | 47175 | 1770 | | |
| 47576 | 47176 | 1771 | | |
| 47584 | 47180 | 1775 | | |
| 47624 | 47087 | 1673 | | |
| 47627 | 47273 | 1974 | | |
| 47628 | 47078 | 1663 | | |
| 47633 | 47083 | 1668 | | |
| 47634 | 47158 | 1751 | | |
| 47645 | 47075 | 1659 | | |
| 47676 | 47586 | 47042 | 1623 | |
| 47677 | 47617 | 47149 | 1742 | |
| 47702 | 47504 | 1947 | | |
| 47704 | 47495 | 1937 | | |
| 47706 | 47494 | 1936 | | |
| 47707 | 47506 | 1949 | | |
| 47708 | 47516 | 1968 | | |
| 47709 | 47499 | 1942 | | |
| 47710 | 47496 | 1939 | | |
| 47711 | 47498 | 1941 | | |
| 47713 | 47510 | 1954 | | |
| 47716 | 47507 | 1957 | | |
| 47717 | 47497 | 1940 | | |
| 47721 | 47557 | 47024 | 1591 | |
| 47722 | 47558 | 47027 | 1599 | |
| 47725 | 47567 | 47044 | 1625 | |
| 47726 | 47568 | 47045 | 1626 | |
| 47733 | 47582 | 47170 | 1765 | |
| 47734 | 47583 | 47172 | 1767 | |
| 47736 | 47587 | 47263 | 1963 | |
| 47737 | 47588 | 47178 | 1773 | |
| 47738 | 47592 | 47171 | 1766 | |
| 47741 | 47597 | 47026 | 1597 | |
| 47742 | 47598 | 47182 | 1777 | |
| 47743 | 47599 | 47177 | 1772 | |
| 47745 | 47603 | 47267 | 1967 | |
| 47747 | 47615 | 47252 | 1929 | |
| 47750 | 47626 | 47082 | 1667 | |
| 47756 | 47644 | 47246 | 1923 | |
| 47757 | 47585 | 47184 | 1779 | |
| 47758 | 47517 | 1975 | | |
| 47759 | 47559 | 47028 | 1605 | |
| 47762 | 47573 | 47173 | 1768 | |
| 47763 | 47581 | 47169 | 1764 | |
| 47764 | 47630 | 47041 | 1622 | |
| 47766 | 47642 | 47040 | 1621 | |
| 47767 | 47641 | 47086 | 1672 | |
| 47774 | 47801 | 47551 | 47153 | 1746 |
| 47775 | 47531 | 47974 | 1584 | |
| 47777 | 47243 | 47636 | 1920 | |
| 47778 | 47842 | 47606 | 47081 | 1666 |
| 47779 | 47838 | 47612 | 47080 | 1665 |
| 47780 | 47836 | 47618 | 47030 | 1609 |
| 47781 | 47808 | 47653 | 47088 | 1674 |
| 47782 | 47824 | 47602 | 47185 | 1780 |
| 47783 | 47809 | 47654 | 47056 | 1640 |
| 47784 | 47819 | 47664 | 47135 | 1727 |
| 47788 | 47833 | 47608 | 47262 | 1962 |
| 47789 | 47671 | 47616 | 47248 | 1925 |
| 47791 | 47675 | 47595 | 47268 | 1969 |
| 47803 | 47553 | 47260 | 1956 | |
| 47829 | 47619 | 47264 | 1964 | |
| 47837 | 47611 | 47166 | 1761 | |
| 47839 | 47621 | 47136 | 1728 | |
| 47844 | 47556 | 47020 | 1583 | |
| 47849 | 47570 | 47048 | 1630 | |
| 47850 | 47648 | 47151 | 1744 | |
| 47852 | 47646 | 47074 | 1658 | |
| 47901 | 47601 | 47046 | 1628 | |
| 47971 | 97480 | 47480 | 1616 | |
| 47972 | 97545 | 47545 | 1646 | |
| 47973 | 97561 | 47561 | 47034 | 1614 |
| 47976 | 47546 | 1747 | | |
| 47981 | 47364 | 1883 | | |

**Class 50 Type 4 diesel-electric Co-Co**

| | |
|---|---|
| 50001 | 401 |
| 50003 | 403 |
| 50004 | 404 |
| 50005 | 405 |
| 50006 | 406 |
| 50009 | 409 |
| 50010 | 410 |
| 50011 | 411 |
| 50012 | 412 |
| 50013 | 413 |
| 50014 | 414 |
| 50016 | 416 |
| 50018 | 418 |
| 50020 | 420 |
| 50022 | 422 |
| 50023 | 423 |

| | |
|---|---|
| 50024 | 424 |
| 50025 | 425 |
| 50028 | 428 |
| 50032 | 432 |
| 50034 | 434 |
| 50036 | 436 |
| 50037 | 437 |
| 50038 | 438 |
| 50039 | 439 |
| 50040 | 440 |
| 50041 | 441 |
| 50043 | 443 |
| 50045 | 445 |
| 50046 | 446 |
| 50047 | 447 |
| 50048 | 448 |

**Class 52 Type 4 diesel-hydraulic C-C**

1000
1001
1002
1003
1004
1005
1006
1007
1008
1009
1011
1012
1014
1016
1017
1018
1019
1020
1021
1022
1024
1025
1026
1027
1028
1029
1030
1031
1032
1033
1034
1035
1036
1037
1038
1039
1040
1042
1043
1044
1045
1046
1047
1049
1050
1051
1052
1053
1054
1055
1056
1057
1058
1059
1060
1061
1063
1064
1065
1066
1067
1068
1069
1070
1071
1072
1073

**Class 53 Type 4 diesel-electric Co-Co**

| | |
|---|---|
| 1200 | 0280 |

**Class 55 Type 5 diesel-electric Co-Co**

| | |
|---|---|
| 55001 | 9001 |
| 55003 | 9003 |
| 55004 | 9004 |
| 55005 | 9005 |
| 55006 | 9006 |
| 55007 | 9007 |
| 55008 | 9008 |
| 55010 | 9010 |
| 55011 | 9011 |
| 55012 | 9012 |
| 55013 | 9013 |
| 55014 | 9014 |
| 55017 | 9017 |
| 55018 | 9018 |
| 55020 | 9020 |
| 55021 | 9021 |

**Class 56 Type 5 diesel-electric Co-Co**

56001
56002
56004
56005
56008
56010
56011
56012
56013
56014
56015
56016
56017
56019
56020
56021
56022
56023
56024
56025
56026
56027
56028
56029
56030
56033
56034
56035
56036
56039
56040
56041
56042
56043
56044
56046
56047
56048
56050
56052
56053
56054
56055
56056
56058

**Class 56 Type 5 diesel-electric Co-Co (Continued...)**
56059
56061
56062
56063
56064
56066
56067
56068
56070
56071
56072
56073
56074
56075
56076
56079
56080
56082
56083
56084
56085
56086
56088
56089
56092
56093
56095
56099
56100
56102
56107
56108
56109
56110
56111
56112
56114
56116
56118
56119
56120
56121
56122
56123
56126
56127
56129
56130
56131
56132
56133
56134
56135

**Class 58 Type 5 diesel-electric Co-Co**
58002
58003
58008
58014
58017
58019
58028
58037
58045

**Class 66 Type 5 diesel-electric Co-Co**

| | |
|---|---|
| 66521 | |
| 66734 | 66402 |

**Class 70 Type 5 diesel-electric Co-Co**
70012

**Class 70 750V DC electric Co-Co**

| | |
|---|---|
| 20001 | CC1 |
| 20002 | CC2 |
| 20003 | |

**Class 71 750V DC electric Bo-Bo**

| | | |
|---|---|---|
| 71002 | E5002 | |
| 71003 | E5018 | E5003 |
| 71004 | E5004 | |
| 71005 | E5020 | E5005 |
| 71006 | E5022 | E5006 |
| 71007 | E5007 | |
| 71008 | E5008 | |
| 71009 | E5009 | |
| 71010 | E5010 | |
| 71011 | E5011 | |
| 71012 | E5012 | |
| 71013 | E5013 | |
| 71014 | E5014 | |

Note: Numbers E5003/05/06 were used twice

**Class 73 750V DC Electro-diesel Bo-Bo**

| | | |
|---|---|---|
| 73004 | E6004 | |
| 73106 | E6012 | |
| 73108 | E6014 | |
| 73111 | E6017 | |
| 73115 | E6021 | |
| | E6027 | |
| 73126 | E6033 | |
| 73131 | E6038 | |
| 73132 | E6039 | |
| 73203 | 73127 | E6024 |

**Class 74 750V DC Electro-diesel Bo-Bo**

| | | | |
|---|---|---|---|
| 74001 | E6101 | E5015 | |
| 74002 | E6102 | E5016 | |
| 74003 | E6103 | E5006 | |
| 74004 | E6104 | E5000 | E5024 |
| 74005 | E6105 | E5019 | |
| 74006 | E6106 | E5023 | |
| 74007 | E6107 | E5003 | |
| 74008 | E6108 | E5005 | |
| 74009 | E6109 | E5017 | |
| 74010 | E6110 | E5021 | |

**Class 76 1,500V DC electric Bo+Bo**

| | | |
|---|---|---|
| | E26000 | 6700 |
| 76001 | E26001 | |
| 76002 | E26002 | |
| 76003 | 76036 | E26036 |
| 76004 | E26004 | |
| | E26005 | |
| 76006 | E26006 | |
| 76007 | E26007 | |
| 76008 | E26008 | |
| 76009 | E26009 | |
| 76010 | E26010 | |
| 76011 | E26011 | |
| 76012 | E26012 | |
| 76013 | E26013 | |
| 76014 | E26014 | |
| 76015 | E26015 | |
| 76016 | E26016 | |
| | E26017 | |
| | E26019 | |
| 76021 | E26021 | |
| 76022 | E26022 | |
| 76023 | E26023 | |
| 76024 | E26024 | |
| 76025 | E26025 | |
| 76026 | E26026 | |
| 76027 | E26027 | |
| 76028 | E26028 | |
| 76029 | E26029 | |
| 76030 | E26030 | |
| | E26031 | |
| 76031 | 76044 | E26044 |
| 76032 | E26032 | |
| 76033 | E26033 | |
| 76034 | E26034 | |
| | E26035 | |
| 76035 | 76018 | E26018 |

| | | |
|---|---|---|
| 76036 | 76003 | E26003 |
| 76037 | E26037 | |
| 76038 | 76050 | E26050 |
| 76039 | 76048 | E26048 |
| 76040 | E26040 | |
| 76041 | E26041 | |
| | E26042 | |
| 76043 | E26043 | |
| | E26045 | |
| 76046 | E26046 | |
| 76047 | E26047 | |
| 76048 | 76039 | E26039 |
| 76049 | E26049 | |
| 76050 | 76038 | E26038 |
| 76051 | E26051 | |
| 76052 | E26052 | |
| 76053 | E26053 | |
| 76054 | E26054 | |
| 76055 | E26055 | |
| 76056 | E26056 | |
| 76057 | E26057 | |

Note: Numbers 76003/036/038/039/048/050 were used twice

**Class 77 1,500V DC electric Co-Co**

| | |
|---|---|
| | E27005 |
| 1503 | E27004 |
| 1504 | E27006 |
| 1506 | E27002 |

**Class 81 25kV AC electric Bo-Bo**

| | |
|---|---|
| 81001 | E3001 |
| | E3002 |
| 81003 | E3004 |
| 81004 | E3005 |
| 81005 | E3006 |
| 81006 | E3007 |
| 81007 | E3008 |
| | E3009 |
| 81008 | E3010 |
| 81009 | E3011 |
| 81010 | E3012 |
| 81011 | E3013 |
| 81012 | E3014 |
| 81013 | E3015 |
| 81014 | E3016 |
| 81015 | E3017 |
| 81016 | E3018 |
| | E3019 |
| 81017 | E3020 |
| 81018 | E3021 |
| 81019 | E3022 |
| 81020 | E3023 |
| 81021 | E3096 |
| 81022 | E3097 |

**Class 82 25kV AC electric Bo-Bo**

| | |
|---|---|
| | E3046 |
| 82001 | E3047 |
| 82002 | E3048 |
| 82003 | E3049 |
| 82004 | E3050 |
| 82005 | E3051 |
| 82006 | E3052 |
| 82007 | E3053 |
| | E3055 |

**Class 83 25kV AC electric Bo-Bo**

| | | |
|---|---|---|
| 83001 | E3024 | |
| 83002 | E3025 | |
| 83003 | E3026 | |
| 83004 | E3027 | |
| 83005 | E3028 | |
| 83006 | E3029 | |
| 83007 | E3030 | |
| 83008 | E3031 | |
| 83009 | E3032 | |
| 83010 | E3033 | |
| 83011 | E3034 | |
| 83013 | E3098 | E3303 |
| 83014 | E3099 | E3304 |
| 83015 | E3100 | |

**Class 84 25kV AC electric Bo-Bo**

| | | |
|---|---|---|
| 84002 | E3037 | |
| 84003 | E3038 | |
| 84004 | E3039 | |
| 84005 | E3040 | |
| 84006 | E3041 | |
| 84007 | E3042 | |
| 84008 | E3043 | |
| 84009 | E3044 | ADB968021 |
| 84010 | E3045 | |

**Class 85 25kV AC electric Bo-Bo**

| | | |
|---|---|---|
| 85001 | E3056 | |
| 85002 | E3057 | |
| 85005 | E3060 | |
| 85008 | E3063 | |
| 85013 | E3068 | |
| 85014 | E3069 | |
| 85015 | E3070 | |
| 85017 | E3072 | |
| 85018 | E3073 | |
| 85019 | E3074 | |
| 85020 | E3075 | |
| 85022 | E3077 | |
| 85023 | E3078 | |
| 85025 | E3080 | |
| 85026 | E3081 | |
| 85027 | E3082 | |
| 85028 | E3083 | |
| 85029 | E3084 | |
| 85030 | E3085 | |
| 85031 | E3086 | |
| 85033 | E3088 | |
| 85034 | E3089 | |
| 85037 | E3092 | |
| 85038 | E3093 | |
| 85039 | E3094 | |
| 85040 | E3095 | |
| 85102 | 85009 | E3064 |
| 85103 | 85010 | E3065 |
| 85104 | 85012 | E3067 |
| 85105 | 85016 | E3071 |
| 85106 | 85021 | E3076 |
| 85107 | 85024 | E3079 |
| 85108 | 85032 | E3087 |
| 85109 | 85035 | E3090 |
| 85110 | 85036 | E3091 |
| 85111 | 85004 | E3059 |
| 85112 | 85007 | E3062 |
| 85113 | 85003 | E3058 |
| 85114 | 85011 | E3066 |

**Class 86 25kV AC electric Bo-Bo**

| | | | | |
|---|---|---|---|---|
| 86102 | 86202 | E3150 | | |
| 86103 | 86203 | E3143 | | |
| 86204 | E3173 | | | |
| 86206 | E3184 | | | |
| 86207 | E3179 | | | |
| 86208 | E3141 | | | |
| 86209 | E3125 | | | |
| 86211 | E3147 | | | |
| 86212 | E3151 | | | |
| 86214 | E3106 | | | |
| 86216 | E3166 | | | |
| 86219 | E3196 | | | |
| 86220 | E3156 | | | |
| 86221 | E3132 | | | |
| 86222 | 86502 | E3131 | | |
| 86223 | E3158 | | | |
| 86224 | E3134 | | | |
| 86225 | E3164 | | | |
| 86226 | E3162 | | | |
| 86227 | E3117 | | | |
| 86230 | E3168 | | | |
| 86236 | E3133 | | | |
| 86237 | E3197 | | | |
| 86238 | E3116 | | | |
| 86239 | 86507 | E3169 | | |
| 86240 | E3127 | | | |
| 86241 | 86508 | E3121 | | |
| 86243 | E3181 | | | |
| 86244 | E3178 | | | |
| 86245 | E3182 | | | |
| 86246 | 86505 | E3149 | | |
| 86247 | E3192 | | | |
| 86249 | E3161 | | | |
| 86252 | E3101 | | | |
| 86254 | 86047 | E3142 | | |
| 86255 | 86042 | E3154 | | |
| 86256 | 86040 | E3135 | | |
| 86257 | 86043 | E3139 | | |
| 86258 | 86501 | 86046 | E3140 | |
| 86261 | 86041 | E3118 | | |
| 86416 | 86316 | 86016 | E3109 | |
| 86417 | 86317 | 86017 | E3146 | |
| 86419 | 86319 | 86019 | E3120 | |
| 86425 | 86325 | 86025 | E3186 | |
| 86426 | 86326 | 86026 | E3195 | |
| 86429 | 86329 | 86029 | E3200 | |
| 86430 | 86030 | E3105 | | |
| 86602 | 86402 | 86002 | E3170 | |
| 86603 | 86403 | 86003 | E3115 | |
| 86606 | 86406 | 86006 | E3112 | |
| 86611 | 86411 | 86311 | 86011 | E3171 |
| 86615 | 86415 | 86315 | 86015 | E3123 |
| 86618 | 86418 | 86318 | 86018 | E3163 |
| 86620 | 86420 | 86320 | 86020 | E3114 |
| 86621 | 86421 | 86321 | 86021 | E3157 |
| 86623 | 86423 | 86323 | 86023 | E3152 |
| 86631 | 86431 | 86031 | E3188 | |
| 86633 | 86433 | 86033 | E3198 | |
| 86634 | 86434 | 86034 | E3187 | |
| 86635 | 86435 | 86035 | E3124 | |
| 86636 | 86436 | 86036 | E3160 | |
| 86902 | 86210 | E3190 | | |

Note: Number 86501 was used twice by 86258 and 86608 (the latter still in traffic)

**Class 87 25kV AC electric Bo-Bo**

87005
87011
87015
87016
87018
87021
87024
87027
87030
87031
87032
87101

**Various departmental locos**

| | |
|---|---|
| 97020 | 20 |
| 97650 | PWM650 |
| 97651 | PWM651 |
| 97652 | PWM652 |
| 97653 | PWM653 |
| 97654 | PWM654 |
| 97701 | M61136 |
| 97702 | M61139 |
| 97703 | M61182 |
| 97704 | M61185 |
| 97705 | M61184 |
| 97706 | M61189 |
| 97707 | M61166 |
| 97708 | M61173 |
| 97709 | M61172 |
| 97710 | M61175 |
| ED1 | |
| ED2 | |
| ED3 | |
| ED4 | |
| ED5 | |
| ED6 | |
| ED7 | |
| ED10 | |
| ZM9 | |

# Livery codes

ADZ Advenza Freight blue
AGA Abellio Greater Anglia white
AGI Aggregates industries turquoise and silver
ANG Anglia Railways turquoise
ATW Arriva Trains Wales turquoise, unbranded
AVD AV Dawson red
BAF Bardon Aggregates blue with Freightliner branding
BBM Battle of Britain Memorial Flight graphics
BDB Boston Docks blue
BLE Unspecified plain blue
BLK British Railways black
BLL British Rail 'large logo' blue with yellow cabs
BLU British Rail blue yellow cabsides
BMT Bulmarket red
BRB British Rail blue with full yellow ends
BRE British Rail blue with large numbers and emblems
BRF British Rail blue with Union flags
BRL British Rail blue large logo blue with black roof
BRP British Rail blue grey prototype HST
BRW British Rail blue with wasp stripes
BRY British Railways blue with Foster Yeoman branding
BRZ BZK BR blue
BYP British Rail blue with small yellow panels
BZK BZK (БЪлгарска ЖеиезолЪтна Компания) green and yellow
CAL Caledonian Sleeper blue
CAS Castle Cement light grey
CCE Civil engineers' grey/yellow 'Dutch'
CCT Civil engineers' grey/yellow 'Dutch' with Transrail logos
CEL Celsa black with orange cab
CFD Chemins de fer Départméntaux orange
COL Colas Rail Freight orange, yellow and black
CON Continental rail blue
COR Corus silver
COT BZK Cotswold Rail silver
COY Corus yellow
CRS Chiltern Railways silver/grey
CSM Continental Railway Solution maroon
DBC DB Cargo red
DL Dean Lane (Manchester)
DBM DB Cargo Manager's Train silver
DBR Deutsche Bahn all over red
DBS DB Schenker red
DCG Devon & Cornwall Railways green
DCR DC Rail grey
DEP Departmental grey
DGB BZK DRS blue with orange cab
DNS Nederlandse Spoorwegen grey/yellow
DRA Drax silver
DRC DRS blue with Compass logos
DRE DRS blue with new Compass logos (Class 88)
DRN DRS blue with new Compass logos
DRS DRS blue original
DRU DRS blue, unbranded
DRX DRS blue with smaller Compass logos
DST Deanside Transit lilac
DSY Desert Sand with yellow panels
EBY Electric blue yellow panels
ECR Euro Cargo Rail light grey
EMB East Midlands Trains blue
EMY GBRf with Emily Woodman graphics
EPX Europhoenix silver
ETF Eurovia Travaux Ferroviaires yellow
EUE Eurostar grey with EWS logos
EUK Eurostar grey
EWS EWS maroon and gold
FER Fertis grey
FEU Fertis grey unbranded
FGA First Great Western blue with advertising wrap
FGB First Great Western blue
FGO Fragonset black unbranded
FGU First Great Western blue unbranded
FGS First Great Western 'special' graphics
FLG Freightliner two tone grey
FLR Freightliner green with yellow cabs
FLS Freightliner green with Shanks advertising
FLY Floyd black

FPG Freightliner green unbranded
FPH Freightliner 'Powerhaul' green, yellow and grey
FRG Fragonset black
FSR First ScotRail blue
FTF Fall the Fallen graphics
GBF GB Railfreight blue and orange
GBR GB Railfreight blue and orange Europorte style
GBO GB Railfreight blue and orange original style
GBZ GB Railfreight blue and orange with minor variations
GCR Grand Central black
GFY British Railways green full yellow ends
GLA Glaxo chemicals blue and dark grey
GOP Golden Ochre with yellow panels
GNY British Railways green no yellow ends
GRE Unspecified plain green
GWS British Rail green with wasp stripes
GWT Great Western Trains all over green
GWR Great Western Railway green
GYP British Railways green with yellow panels
HAN Hanson aggregates blue and silver
HAR 'Harry Patch' black graphics
HNO Harry Needle Railroad Company orange
HOP Hope Construction white with purple solebar
HST Original blue, grey, yellow HST
HUN Hunslet green
ICM BR InterCity 'Mainline'
ICO BR InterCity original style
ICS BR InterCity Swallow style
IGX BR InterCity Gatwick Express
IOS BR InterCity original with ScotRail branding
IND Industrial livery
JUB DB Cargo Diamond Jubilee silver
JFU Jarvis Fastline unbranded grey
KBR Knorr Bremse green, white and blue
LAB 'Laira' blue with grey roof
LAM Lamco orange
LHO Loadhaul original
LNR BZK LNWR blackberry black
LNW LNWR grey
LON London Midland black and green
LOR Loram advertising graphics
LUB GBRf London Transport Museum black with graphics
LUW GBRf London Transport Museum white with graphics
MAA DB Cargo with WH Malcolm graphics
MAL WH Malcolm, green, yellow and blue
MAR Lakeside & Haverthwaite Railway lined maroon
MEW Mainline Freight blue with EWS logos
MFY Maroon with full yellow ends
MID Midland Railway maroon
MLB Mainline Freight blue
MRM Metropolitan Railway maroon
MRT GBRf Maritime blue
MSC GBRf with Medite Sorrento graphics
MWS Maroon with wasp stripes
MYP Maroon with yellow panels
NBU Northern Belle umber and cream unbranded
NCB National Coal Board blue
NOB Northern Belle umber and cream
NOR Northern purple
NRA National Railway Museum advertising wrap
NRB National Railway Museum light blue
NRM National Railway Museum maroon
NRY Network Rail yellow
NSD Network SouthEast revised darker blue
NSE BZK Network SouthEast red white and blue
NSO Network SouthEast original with white window frames
NSR Network SouthEast revised with blue window frames
OXB Oxford blue
PUL Pullman umber and cream
RCA Railcare red white and blue
RCG Railcare grey and white
RED Unspecified plain red
REG Regional Railways blue and grey
RES Rail Express systems red and dark grey
REW Railfreight Distribution 'European' two tone grey with EWS logos
RFD Railfreight Distribution two tone grey with RfD logos
RFE Railfreight Distribution 'European' two tone grey with RfD logos

RFO Railfreight Original grey
RFS RFS grey
RMS RMS Locotec blue
ROG Rail Operations Group blue
ROY Royal Scotsman plum
RSR Railfreight Red stripe
RTO Royal Train plum
RTP Royal Train Res style
SCR ScotRail Saltire blue
SIL Silverlink green, purple and white
SOU Southern green and white
SPE Bombardier special purple, green, blue and red
STO Stobart Rail advertising
SWU South West Trains blue unbranded
TAB Tata Blue
TAS Tata Silver
TEW Trainload grey with EWS logos
TLA Trainload grey with Aggregates logos
TLC Trainload grey with Coal logos
TLH Trainload grey with Loadhaul logos
TLM Trainload grey with Metals logos
TMF Trainload grey with Mainline Freight logo
TMT Transmart Trains green
TTG Two tone unbranded Railfreight grey
TRN Transrail grey
TSO TSO yellow
UKR UK Rail Leasing grey with yellow cabs
UND Undercoat/unpainted/primer
VEA Virgin Trains red with advertising branding
VEC Virgin Trains East Coast
VFS Virgin Trains Flying Scotsman
VIR Virgin Trains red
WCR West Coast Railways maroon with yellow panels
XCT CrossCountry Trains

# Pool codes

| | |
|---|---|
| ATLO | Alstom Traincare Locomotives |
| ATZZ | Alstom Traincare Locomotives For Disposal |
| AWCA | West Coast Railway Operational Diesel Locomotives |
| AWCX | West Coast Railway Stored Diesel Locomotives |
| BREL | Boden Rail Engineering |
| CDJD | Central Services/Serco Railtest Ex Serco Shunters |
| CFOL | Class 50 Operations Ltd |
| CFSL | Class 40 Stored Locos |
| COFS | Colas Rail Freight |
| COLO | Colas Rail Freight Hire Locomotives |
| COLS | Colas Rail Freight Stored Locomotives |
| COTS | Colas Rail Freight Locomotives For Refurbishing |
| DBLX | Deltic Preservation Society |
| DDIN | Freightliner Shunter Fleet |
| DFGH | Freightliner Heavy Haul |
| DFGI | Freightliner Intermodal |
| DFHG | Freightliner Heavy Haul |
| DFHH | Freightliner Heavy Haul |
| DFHJ | Freightliner Heavy Haul Limited Use |
| DFIM | Freightliner Intermodal Modified |
| DFIN | Freightliner Intermodal Low Emission |
| DFLC | Freightliner Intermodal |
| DFLH | Freightliner Heavy Haul |
| DFNC | Freightliner Awaiting Maintenance |
| DHLT | Freightliner Stored/Not In Main Line Use Locomotives |
| EFOO | First Great Western FGW Class 57/6 |
| EFPC | First Great Western FGW Class 43 |
| EFSH | First Great Western FGW Shunters |
| EHPC | Arriva CrossCountry HST Power Cars |
| EJLO | London Midland Shunters |
| ELRD | East Lancashire Railway Operational Locomotives |
| EMPC | East Midlands Trains HST Power Cars |
| EMSL | East Midlands Trains Shunters |
| EPEX | Europhoenix For Scrap/Export |
| EPUK | Europhoenix UK Locomotives |
| GBBR | GBRf Class 73/9 – Brush Repowered |
| GBBT | GBRf UK Cab – Long Range Fuel Tanks |
| GBCH | GBRf Caledonian Sleeper |
| GBCS | GBRf Re-Engineered |
| GBEB | GBRf Euro Cab – Long Range Fuel Tanks |
| GBED | GBRf Electro Diesel Locos For Hire |
| GBEE | GBRf On Hire Class 20 |
| GBEL | GBRf Euro Cab -Standard Fuel Tanks |
| GBET | GBRf Stored Locos |
| GBFM | GBRf RETB Fitted Locomotives |
| GBHN | GBRf Long Term Hire Locomotives |
| GBLT | GBRf UK Cab – Standard Fuel Tanks |
| GBNB | GBRf New Build Locos |
| GBNR | GBRf For Network Rail Use |
| GBRT | GBRf Restricted Locos |
| GBSL | GBRf Caledonian Sleepers |
| GBST | GBRf Caledonian Sleepers/Channel Tunnel |
| GBWM | GBRf Shunting Duties |
| GBYH | GBRf General Pool |
| GCHP | Grand Central HST Power Cars |
| GPSS | Eurostar UK Operate From TI (DBC Maintained) |
| GROG | Rail Operations Group Operational Locos |
| HBSH | Virgin Trains East Coast On Hire To VTEC |
| HISE | Rail Vehicle Engineering East Midlands Trains Shunters |
| HTLX | Hanson Traction Operational Locomotives |
| HYWD | South West Trains Thunderbird Locos |
| IANA | Greater Anglia Loco Fleet |
| IECA | Virgin Trains East Coast Operational Locomotives |
| IECP | Virgin Trains East Coast HST power cars |
| KDSD | Bombardier Doncaster |
| MBDL | Non TOC Private Owner – Diesel locos |
| MBED | Non TOC Private Owner – Class 73 |
| MBEL | Non TOC Private Owner – Electric locos |
| MOLO | RT Rail Limited Hired Fleet Shunter locos |
| MRLO | RMS Locotec Ex-FM Rail Operational Locos |
| MRLS | RMS Locotec Ex-FM Rail Stored locos |
| MRSO | RMS Locotec Ex-FM Rail Operational Shunters |
| NRLO | Nemesis Rail Locomotives On Hire |

NRLS Nemesis Rail Ex-FM Rail Stored locos
QACL Network Rail Load Bank
QADD Network Rail Diesel Locos
QCAR Network Rail HST Power Cars
QETS Network Rail European Signalling
RCZH Knorr Bremse Rail Systems Springburn Works Shunters
RCZN Knorr Bremse Rail Systems Wolverton Works Shunters
RFSH Wabtec Rail Locomotives
RMSX RMS Locotec Locomotives
RTSO Riviera Trains Operational Shunters
RVLO Railway Vehicle Engineering Derby Operational Locomotives
SAXL Eversholt Rail Off Lease Locos
SBXL Porterbrook Leasing Off Lease Locos
SCXL Angel Train Contracts Off Lease Locos
TTLS Traditional Traction/Railway Support Services
UKRL UK Rail Leasing On Lease
UMRM UK Rail Leasing Not Main Line
UKRS UK Rail Leasing Stored
WAAC DB Cargo UK
WABC DB Cargo UK RETB Fitted
WAWC DB Cargo UK Arriva Wales Hire
WBAE DB Cargo UK Fitted With Stop/Start Technology
WBAR DB Cargo UK Remote Condition Monitoring Equipment
WBAT DB Cargo UK General
WBBE DB Cargo UK RETB & Stop/Start Technology Fitted
WBBT DB Cargo UK RETB Fitted
WBLE DB Cargo UK Lickey Bankers With Stop/Start Technology
WBLT DB Cargo UK
WBTT DB Cargo UK RHTT – Tripcock Fitted
WCAT DB Cargo UK Standard Fuel Range
WCBT DB Cargo UK Extended Fuel Rail
WDAM DB Cargo UK
WEAC DB Cargo UK
WFBC DB Cargo UK HS1 Equipped
WGEA DB Cargo UK Euro Cargo Rail
WGEE DB Cargo UK Eastern Europe
WGEP DB Cargo UK Poland
WQAA DB Cargo UK Locomotives Stopped Serviceable – Group 1A
WQAB DB Cargo UK Stored Locomotives Group 1B
WQBA DB Cargo UK Stored Locomotives Stored Serviceable – Group 2
WQCA DB Cargo UK Stored Locos For Component Recovery – Group 3
WQDA DB Cargo UK Stored Locomotives Surplus – Group 4
XHAC Direct Rail Services Operational Locos – ETS Equipped
XHCC Direct Rail Services Operational Locos – Northern (Cumbrian Coast Workings)
XHCE Direct Rail Services Hire To Chiltern Railways
XHCK Direct Rail Services Operational Locos
XHIM Direct Rail Services Intermodal Locos
XHNC Direct Rail Services Nuclear Traffic
XHSS Direct Rail Services Stored Locos
XHTP Direct Rail Services Locos For Transpennine Express
XHVE Direct Rail Services Vossloh Locos
XHVT Direct Rail Services West Coast Thunderbird Locos
XYPA Mendip Rail Operational Locomotives
XYPO Mendip Rail Operational Locomotives

# Depot codes

| Code | Depot / Operator |
|---|---|
| AB | Albacete (Spain)<br>Continental Rail |
| AC | Alicante (Spain)<br>Transfesa |
| AH | Asfordby Technical Centre<br>Network Rail |
| AN | Allerton<br>Alstom |
| AT | Attercliffe<br>European Metal Recycling |
| AZ | Alizay Nr. Rouen – France<br>DB Cargo |
| BB | Billingham<br>Sembcorp Utilities |
| BD | Boston Docks<br>Victoria Group |
| BH | Barrow Hill Roundhouse |
| BK | Bristol Barton Hill<br>LNWR |
| BL | Loughborough Falcon Works<br>Wabtec/Bruch Traction |
| BM | Bournemouth West<br>South Western Railway |
| BN | Bounds Green<br>Virgin Trains East Coast |
| BO | Bo'ness<br>Scottish Railway Preservation Society |
| BQ | Bury<br>East Lancs Railway |
| BS | Bescot<br>DB Cargo |
| BU | Burton-On-Trent<br>Nemesis Rail |
| BZ | Sofia, Bulgaria<br>BZK БЪлгарска ЖеиезолЪтна Компания |
| CB | Crewe Basford Hall<br>Network Rail |
| CC | Cardiff Steelworks<br>Celsa |
| CD | Crewe DMD<br>Locomotive Services Limited |
| CE | Crewe International Electric<br>DB Cargo |
| CF | Cardiff Canton<br>Colas Rail Freight |
| CL | Crewe<br>LNWR |
| CM | Cambridge<br>Arriva CrossCountry |
| CO | Coquelles (France)<br>Eurotunnel |
| CQ | Crewe<br>Railway Age Trust |
| CP | Crewe Carriage Shed<br>Arriva |
| CR | Crewe Gresty Bridge<br>Direct Rail Services |
| CS | Carnforth<br>West Coast Railways |
| CZ | Burton Central Rivers<br>Bombardier |
| DC | Craiova Romania exported locos<br>DB Cargo |
| DD | Daventry International Railfreight Terminal<br>Malcolm Rail |
| DF | Derby RTC<br>Loram (UK) |
| DG | Dagenham |
| DK | Konkar Bulgaria exported locos<br>DB Cargo |
| DL | Dean Lane (Manchester) |
| DM | Dollands Moor<br>Eurotunnel |
| DS | Deanside<br>Deanside Transit |
| DY | Derby Etches Park<br>East Midlands Trains |
| EC | Craigentinny<br>Virgin Trains East Coast |
| EG | Liverpool Edge Hill<br>Alstom |
| EK | Shepherdswell<br>East Kent Railway |
| EH | Eastleigh<br>DB Cargo |
| FD | Mobile Maintenance, Mainline Diesels<br>Freightliner |
| FE | Mobile Maintenance, Mainline Electrics<br>Freightliner |
| FG | Garston<br>Ford |
| FP | Mobile Maintenance, Poland<br>Freightliner |

FS Mobile Maintenance, Diesel Shunters
Freightliner
FT Fréthun (France)
DB Cargo
FX Felixstowe
Freightliner
GO Grosmont
North Yorkshire Moors Railway
HA Haymarket
ScotRail
HH Hams Hall
Associated British Ports
HO Hope
Hope Construction
HQ Headquarters
HT Newcastle Heaton
Northern/Grand Central
HUN Hungary
Floyd
IN UK Industrial Sites
IS Inverness
ScotRail
KM Carlisle Kingmoor
Direct Rail Services
KR Kidderminster
Severn Valley Railway
KT Ketton Cement Works
Heidelburg Cement Group
KY Knottingley
DB Cargo
LA Plymouth Laira
Great Western Railway
LD Leeds Midland Road
Freightliner
LE Swansea Landore
Great Western Railway
LG Manchester Longsight Electric
Alstom
LH Barton-Under-Needwood
LH Group Services (Wabtec)
LM Long Marston
Quiton Rail
LO Manchester Longsight Diesel
Alstom
LR Leicester
UK Rail Leasing
LW Longtown (Smalmstown)
MoD
MA Manchester International Traincare
Alstom
MB Middlesbrough
AV Dawson
MD Merehead
Aggregated Industries
MG Margam
DB Cargo
MQ Machen Quarry
Hanson Aggregates
NC Norwich Crown Point
Abellio Greater Anglia
NL Neville Hill
East Midlands Trains
OO Old Oak Common HST
Great Western Railway
OY Oxley
Alstom
PD Teesport
PD Ports
PG Peterborough
GB Railfreight
PM Bristol St. Philip's Marsh
Great Western Railway
PN Rybnik/Poznan – Poland
DB Cargo
PO Polmadie
Alstom
PU Immingham
Puma Energy
PZ Penzance
Great Western Railway
RR Doncaster Roberts Road
EMD/GB Railfreight
RU Rugby Rail Plant
Colas Rail Freight
SB Shrewsbury Coleham Yard
Network Rail
SC Scunthorpe Steelworks
Tata Steel
SE St. Leonards
St Leonards Engineering
SH Southall Railway Centre
West Coast Railways
SI Soho
London Midland
SK Swanwick
Midland Railway Butterley

| | |
|---|---|
| SL | Stewarts Lane<br>Southern |
| SM | Southampton Maritime<br>Freightliner |
| SP | Wigan Springs Branch<br>DB Cargo |
| SS | Shotton Steelworks<br>Tata Steel |
| TC | Toton Training Compound<br>DB Cargo |
| TI | Temple Mills International<br>Eurostar |
| TM | Tyseley Locomotive Works<br>Vintage Trains |
| TO | Toton<br>DB Cargo |
| TR | Trostre Steelworks<br>Tata Steel |
| TS | Tyseley<br>London Midland |
| TX | Thuxton<br>Mid Norfolk Railway |
| TY | Toton Yard<br>DB Cargo |
| WB | Wembley Traincare<br>Alstom |
| WC | Washwood Heath<br>Cemex |
| WD | Widnes<br>Alstom |
| WG | Whitemoor Yard<br>GB Railfreight |
| WH | Washwood Heath<br>Boden Rail Engineering/DC Rail |
| WI | Wishaw<br>Moveright International |
| WN | Willesden<br>GBRf/LOROL |
| WO | Wolsingham<br>Weardale Railway |
| WP | Woippy (France)<br>DB Cargo |
| WQ | Headquarters |
| WR | Leeming Bar<br>Wensleydale Railway |
| WY | Westbury Yard<br>DB Cargo |
| WZ | Warsaw – Poland<br>Freightliner |
| YK | York National Railway Museum |
| ZA | Derby RTC Business Park<br>Loram |
| ZB | Doncaster Works<br>Wabtec |
| ZC | Crewe Works,<br>Bombardier Transportation |
| ZD | Derby Litchurch Lane Works<br>Bombardier Transportation |
| ZG | Eastleigh Works<br>Arlington Fleet Group |
| ZH | Glasgow Springburn, Works,<br>Knorr Bremse Rail Systems |
| ZI | Ilford Level 5 Works<br>Bombardier Transportation |
| ZK | Kilmarnock Works<br>Wabtec |
| ZN | Wolverton Works<br>Knorr Bremse Rail Systems |
| ZO | Kingsbury<br>European Metal Recycling |
| ZR | Rotherham<br>CF Booth Ltd |
| ZS | Wakefield<br>RMS Locotec |
| ZW | Stoke On Trent Works<br>Axiom Rail/Turners/Marcroft |

# Owner codes

ACL AC Locomotive Group
AGI Aggregates Industries
AGO Andrew Goodman
ALS Alstom
ANG Angel Trains
ARV Arriva Group
BEA Beacon Rail
BEV Beaver Sports
BEN Steve Beniston
BOD Neil Boden
CFA Class 50 Alliance
CFP Class 40 Preservation Society
CFS Class 56 Group
COL Colas Rail Freight
CTL Class 20 Locomotive Society
DBC DB Cargo
DCR DC Rail
DPS Deltic Preservation Society
DRS Direct Rail Services
DTG Diesel Traction Group
EEG English Electric Group
EMT East Midlands Trains
EPX Europhoenix
EUK Eurostar
EVS Eversholt Leasing
FIR First Group
FLI Freightliner
GAR Garcia Hanson
GBR GB Railfreight
GWR Great Western Railway
HAN Hanson Aggregates
HJE Howard Johnston
HNR Harry Needle Railroad Company
LES Les Ross
LOL London Overground
LOM Lombard Finance
LON London Midland
LSL Locomotive Services Limited
MAQ Macquarie Group
MOW Michael Owen
NEM Nemesis Rail
NET Network Rail
NRM National Railway Museum
POR Porterbrook
ROG Rail Operations Group
SFG Stratford Class 47 Group
SOA 71A Locomotives
SRP Scottish Railway Preservation Society
STG Scottish Class 37 Group
UKR UK Rail Leasing
VIN Vintage Trains
WCR West Coast Railways

# Spot hire/industrial owners

**Spot hire/industrial owners**

AFS Arlington Fleet Services
AVD AV Dawson
BOM Bombardier
BMT Bulmarket (Bulgaria)
BZK BZK (Българска ЖеиезолЪтна Компания – Bulgaria)
CON Continental Rail Solutions (Hungary)
CRB Chris Beet
EMD Electromotive Diesels
EMR European Metal Recycling
FLY Floyd (Hungary)
ITY Private owner in Italy
KBR Knorr Bremse
LAM Lamco Mining
LOR Loram
NYM North Yorkshire Moors Railway
RSS Railway Support Services (Traditional Traction)
SEC Serco
SLE St Leonards Engineering
TFA Transfesa
TMT Transmart Trains
TLW Tyseley Locomotive Works
VIC Victoria Group (Boston Docks)
WAB Wabtec

# Heritage railway locations

| | |
|---|---|
| ALL | Allely's yard, Studley |
| ALN | Aln Valley Railway |
| AVR | Avon Valley Railway |
| BAT | Battlefield Line |
| BH | Barrow Hill Roundhouse |
| BKR | Bo'ness & Kinneil Railway |
| BIR | Barry Island Railway |
| BLU | Bluebell Railway |
| BRC | Buckingham Railway Centre |
| BWR | Bodmin & Wenford Railway |
| BU | Burton on Trent |
| CAL | Caledonian Railway |
| CHR | Chasewater Railway |
| CHV | Churnet Valley Railway |
| CPR | Chinnor & Princes Risborough Railway |
| CRT | Cambrian Railways Trust |
| CWR | Cholsey & Wallingford Railway |
| CVR | Colne Valley Railway |
| DFR | Dean Forest Railway |
| DAR | Dartmoor Railway |
| DRC | Didcot Railway Centre |
| DVR | Derwent Valley Light Railway |
| EBR | Embsay Steam Railway |
| EDR | Eden Valley Railway |
| EKR | East Kent Railway |
| ELR | East Lancashire Railway |
| EOR | Epping and Ongar Railway |
| ESR | East Somerset Railway |
| EVR | Ecclesbourne Valley Railway |
| FHR | Fawley Hill Railway |
| GWR | Gloucestershire Warwickshire Railway |
| GCR | Great Central Railway |
| GCN | Great Central Railway Nottingham |
| GIR | Gwili Railway |
| IWR | Isle of Wight Steam Railway |
| KWV | Keighley & Worth Valley Railway |
| KES | Kent & East Sussex Railway |
| LHR | Lakeside & Haverthwaite Railway |
| LLR | Llangollen Railway |
| LWR | Lincolnshire Wolds Railway |
| MAL | Private site Malton |
| MHR | Mid Hants Railway |
| MNR | Mid Norfolk Railway |
| MOL | Moreton-on-Lugg |
| MRB | Midland Railway – Butterley |
| MRM | Mangapps Railway Museum |
| NRM | National Railway Museum York |
| NRS | National Railway Museum Shildon |
| NLR | Northampton and Lamport Railway |
| NNR | North Norfolk Railway |
| NVR | Nene Valley Railway |
| NYM | North Yorkshire Moors Railway |
| NTR | North Tyneside Railway |
| PBR | Pontypool & Blaenavon Railway |
| PDR | Paignton & Dartmouth Railway |
| PKR | Peak Rail |
| PVR | Plym Valley Railway |
| RAC | Railway Age Crewe |
| RDR | Royal Deeside Railway |
| RHR | Rushden Heritage Railway |
| RSR | Ribble Steam Railway |
| RVR | Rother Valley Railway |
| SCR | Swindon & Cricklade Railway |
| SDR | South Devon Railway |
| SPA | Spa Valley Railway |
| STM | Stainmoor Railway |
| STR | Strathspey Railway |
| SWR | Swanage Railway |
| SVR | Severn Valley Railway |
| TBR | Trawsfynydd & Blaenau Railway |
| TIT | Titley Junction |
| TSR | Telford Steam Railway |
| VBR | Vale of Berkeley Railway |
| WH | Washwood Heath |
| WIS | Wishaw |
| WEN | Weardale Railway |
| WEA | Wensleydale Railway |
| WSR | West Somerset Railway |